Series by Nikki Karis

Goddogs

Escape the Swamp
(formerly, The Toad Chronicles)

Becoming Grace

For a list of books within each series, see page 267.
Also, visit www.NikkiKaris.com for more information
about the author and her inspiring projects.

GODDOGS

Based on a True Story

Nikki Karis

 Finding Zeni, Inc.

Tarpon Springs, Florida

Published in the United States of America

First Printing, 2021

Finding Zeni, Inc.

Hardback   : 978-1-949244-41-0

Paperback   : 978-1-949244-42-7

E-Book   : 978-1-949244-43-4

Audio Book   : 978-1-949244-44-1

Finding Zeni, Inc.

530 Riverside Drive

Tarpon Springs, Florida 34689

www.NikkiKaris.com

For media inquiries: contact @nikkikaris.com

Dedication

To Picasso, my heart and soul dog:

There will never be another dog like you.
Thank you for 13.5 years of love, loyalty,
and being my creative muse.
I will love you forever.

Adopted: May 2008, at six months old; and
R.I.P., November 15, 2021.

Photos for Book One

To view photos of Karis's amazing Goddogs featured in
book one of the series as well as photos related to the story,

visit: www.petsoulstv.com/goddogs-series/book-one-photos

Table of Contents

Prologue

"To be so high and not high at all."

~ Hope for the Flowers

A Roman named Horace once said that epic poems should start in the middle. Rather than begin "from the egg," he said they should draw the audience into the middle of things as does *The Iliad* when it starts with an argument over women snatched from raids. Horace had a phrase for this: *in medias res*, although I don't think he meant for this to apply to a memoir like mine which reads more like a fairy tale beginning with "once upon a time."

Truth is—the story of my life, whether fairy tale or otherwise, starts in the middle anyway. On November 19, 2006, when I was three months shy of the big 4-0, my life really began—or rather, the second chapter of it.

So...*Once upon a time, I was about to rescue my first dog, and my first dog was about to rescue me. Little did I know, but from that day forward, God would Divinely guide me down a path toward a beautiful new chapter of my life.*

Chapter One

It's a warm Monday morning in Tarpon Springs, Florida, a small town on the coast of the Gulf of Mexico. I was born here, raised here, and still live and work here. Hard to believe, but I never permanently escaped the nest that I grew up in. At least not yet, I haven't managed to.

And right now, I'm driving south to the courthouse in nearby Clearwater to argue a hearing on a tobacco case I've been litigating for the past six months. Yes, I'm one of those: a dreaded lawyer. I say dreaded only because that's what most people think of me, especially practicing personal injury law like I do. Instead, I prefer to see myself more as a savior, at least in this instance where I'm attempting to slay the big, bad tobacco company on behalf of Susan Desuth; or more accurately, her estate comprised of her husband and her kids, because she died three months prior from smoke-induced lung cancer.

When Susan was living, she was a troubled soul, struggling to make sense of the path her life had taken which included two divorces in her early twenties and a suicide attempt during high school. She had other troubles as well. Like myself, she often felt unloved in this sometimes cold, cruel world.

In many ways, though, my troubles seem far greater than hers. In addition to feeling unloved, I've never been married or had any children, despite being beyond my prime. Not to mention, most days I feel totally lost and confused. My pile of troubles is huge when you think about it— unloved, unmarried, childless, lost, confused, and a dreaded lawyer.

Anyway, my point is that something is gravely missing in my life. I feel like I'm supposed to be doing something different, but I have no idea what that is or how to go about it. This feeling never really goes away, as it haunts me, day in, day out. There are nights when I wake up in a panic, having had a nightmare about the current trajectory of my life.

This is odd, really, because at the same time I'm feeling this way, the pistons are pumping full throttle in my law practice. I mean, I'm on fire, handling hundreds upon hundreds of personal injury cases with money flooding into my bank accounts. And my practice, or rather the growth of it, shows absolutely no signs of slowing down any time soon. It could be as "simple" as me having an early mid-life crisis, as I'm thirty-nine years old right now. Or maybe, it's something else.

All I know is that most mornings I wake up exhausted, feeling like everything about my life has been scripted by others—where I live, what I do for a living, who I associate with. Even how I think, feel, speak, and emote seems highly contrived. And my Greek Orthodox religion, well, that wasn't my choice either. It was decided for me long before I exited my mother's womb, at exactly one minute past midnight on the thirtieth of January 1967.

The whole scenario is akin to living inside a box, only the walls aren't tangible ones that I can touch. They're invisible, yet highly prevalent, with my entire life feeling like it's been fabricated by others—by my family members, by my friends, by my business colleagues, and yes, even by some of my enemies. It's completely suffocating at times!

Mind you, I'm fully aware that this box does not exist in a vacuum. Out of it grows a pillar, and the pillar rises high into the sky like the Washington Monument or Jack's beanstalk because it disappears through the clouds. Day in, day out, I find myself climbing, climbing, climbing this pillar with no real idea of what I'm climbing toward. It's totally exhausting, but I tirelessly forge on in my quest to find out what's at the top.

"Shit!" I shout, jamming on the brakes to my Range Rover almost rear-ending the car in front of me. Traffic has suddenly come to a halt. A school bus is stopped up ahead, and a bunch of kids and parents are waiting for the door to open. Kids—they're so innocent and impressionable. Little do they know what perils lie ahead for them in this godforsaken world.

I look into the rearview mirror and pull down my wide-rimmed Tom Ford sunglasses. Pushing aside a few stray hairs, I think I look pretty damn good—like a movie star. I shake my head and pout my lips. Ha!

Then I catch myself and say: "Stop kidding yourself, Nikki," because that's what I always say. Rarely, do I see myself in a flattering light. I have way too much insecurity stuffed inside this hand-tailored blouse and custom-made suit that I'm wearing, which were shipped all the way from China last year.

Today, I've complemented them with my favorite pair of leather booties and matching set of gold and diamond jewelry I bought during a five-day trip to St. Thomas last year. That trip was tons of fun but expensive—very, very expensive. But that pretty much sums up my choice of wardrobe and trips out of the country the past few years—expensive, meaningless, yet the perfect cover jobs for my insecurity.

I continue to wait in traffic and, like a bad habit, return to judging myself. There's a huge crater on my right cheek—wreckage from battling cystic acne that started during my freshman year of college, after the university forced me to undergo a MMR vaccine to stay enrolled. Poor me—I had an adverse reaction to the toxins contained in the vaccine.

The experience wreaked complete havoc on my self-esteem and put a huge damper on my social endeavors, at a critical time in my life. Although I landed a spot in Delta Gamma, one of the top sororities, I felt like an ugly duckling compared to my sorority sisters, most of whom were blonde and buxom with perfectly flawless skin. I hated the way I looked back then and shied away from many social outings. Yeah, I dated here and there, but I never got close enough to any one guy to let him see the real me. I was too embarrassed by how I looked.

To this day, the whole experience still haunts me, especially when I look in a mirror. And although the breakouts stopped two years ago due to a miraculous Divine healing, the emotional scars still remain.

Tears start flowing, and I wipe them back. "Enough, Nikki," I say. "Don't be ridiculous. The just-cried look is the last thing you want to be wearing when you're in the courtroom," which is where I've got to be in thirty-seven minutes.

I've got a tough-girl litigator image to maintain, so I clean up my act. Glancing into the rearview mirror once again, I have a new resolve—jaw set, confidence in check. Ah, perfecto!

Okay, so I don't look like a movie star. But maybe I could pass for a television star from one of those gazillion Netflix series or better yet, a talk show host with my own flair for connecting with people. That's been my dream for as long as I can remember: to be a published author and have my own talk show where I uplift and inspire others.

My desire to help empower others started way back in the third grade, long before the cystic acne reared its ugly head. I remember when Tommy Uphill needed help with a math problem. Math was not his *forte*. Then again, he struggled with most subjects given his dyslexia. But being a math whiz, and caring about Tommy, I was eager to offer him my aid.

Helping people has always been my *forte*—and still is. Ever since my early childhood, it's been a passion calling to my soul: "Jump! Take a leap of faith. Become who you're meant to be."

My father does it almost every single day; he helps others and has set a huge example for me to follow. Changing peoples' lives through his unique gift for making things happen, that's his modus operandi. No matter how difficult someone's situation may be, he never turns anyone away. The words *failure* and *impossible* simply do not exist in his vocabulary.

And that's what I wanted to do for Tommy way back when. I wanted to build a legacy like my father is doing, by helping Tommy with his schoolwork when no one else would—or could. I wanted to give Tommy hope by helping to empower him.

"Tommy, I'm happy to help you," I whispered, hoping our Wicked Witch of a teacher would not hear me.

"That's okay, Nikki. I really don't need any help," he said proudly but rather loudly.

"Are you sure? I don't mind," I whispered even softer.

"Yes, no, um, well, maybe I do."

And then the Wicked Witch heard us; or rather, heard *me*. "Miss Karis, how many times do I have to tell you? Please stop talking. I need for you to see me after class, *again*," she said very sternly.

"Okay," was all I said, lowering my head in shame.

In her eyes, I was an unsatisfactory student, evidenced by the U I received that grading period. Except for that stupid U, I would have received perfect marks. "Nikki is often disrespectful of the classroom environment. She will take it upon herself to assist fellow students without asking my permission first," is what she wrote on my report card.

"That's unfair, teach," I told her rudely. "Why don't you just retire your witchy wart-face and save us all from vomiting!"

Just kidding. That's what I wanted to say when she handed me my report card, and I read it. Instead, I was so devastated that I could barely think much less articulate a smart-aleck comeback, although I never would have talked back to her. My parents taught me better; they taught me to respect persons of authority almost without question.

The incident sliced my skin like a paring knife, carving the first of many scars of insecurity into my still maturing self-esteem. At the age of nine, a part of my childlike innocence had died, as I didn't understand what I had done wrong and still don't, to this day.

Traffic slowly begins to move again, and I am bounced out of my musings, only to be stopped right away by the red light. "Dammit!" I exclaim, pounding my hand on the steering wheel, wondering who I might sue to fix this God-awful traffic.

Chapter Two

Waiting for the light to change, I pull down my sunglasses for a second time and do a quick check of the Rover, making certain it doesn't have a lick of dirt on the inside or anything out of place, as I tend to get anxious when my environment isn't organized and pristine.

Most likely, this is due to obsessive compulsive disorder which I believe I suffer from. Recently, I've read that OCD is caused from a lack of self-esteem; or maybe, the article said that OCD causes low self-esteem. Either way, all I know is that there isn't a lick of dirt inside the Rover, and this makes me incredibly happy.

I know, I know, I sound incredibly vain but rest assured, vanity isn't what is in the driver's seat of my life these days. It's actually quite the opposite. Deep-rooted insecurity long ago took control of the wheel, after decades of insults and injuries that never seem to go away, fully.

Neurosis? Well, that's a different story. The verdict's still out.

I only wish I had the self-confidence to see myself as a television star. With my mixed Greek blood, brown eyes, dark eyebrows, and the smattering of freckles on my high cheekbones from my mother's English side, I could easily be... Well, it doesn't matter, does it? I will never be that star. Never.

Oh, okay, if you must know, I do occasionally get confused for that actress on the TV show *Weeds*. What's her name? Ha! It's Mary-Louise Parker—like I don't know. Except, she's not Greek like I am; at least, I don't think she is.

"No, no, I'm not Mary-Louise," I say to anyone who might be looking at me for too long. "I'm just the girl who, in fifth grade, was handed a crown of thorns by her best friends for stepping outside the lunch line to say 'hello' to a boy one of them was going out with."

Seriously, I said that to a guy one time in the Tampa International Airport when he stopped me to ask if I was Mary-Louise. He just looked at me like I was nuts. Like really, fifth grade? What on God's green earth would drive eleven-year-old girls to be so vicious?

Or maybe I should have said to him, "Hey, I'm the girl who, in eighth grade, arrived at school to find three-hundred girls wearing, 'I Hate Nikki' pins."

Yeah, that incident was a tad bit painful, all right. Suzanne, the girl who started the whole pin-hating campaign, disliked me with a vengeance. From what I understand, she stayed up the entire night before, cutting the pins out of colored construction paper and writing "I.H.N." on them. The next morning, she passed the pins out to all the girls at school. Only one of my best friends refused to wear one. The rest of my so-called best friends, well, they showed their true colors.

Wait! I almost forgot. Here's one more zinger for the guy in the airport: "I'm the girl who, when I ran for class president in tenth grade, students ran a campaign against." "OUST NIKKI!" their signs said in big fat black Magic Marker. The signs were plastered all over the school—everywhere. Not an empty space was spared. It was a humiliating experience; that's for sure.

You know, I really should have stolen the bullies' thunder by having one of those planes fly by pulling a long "OUST NIKKI" banner. That sure would have shown them—all those enemies, haters, and detractors, putting me down and humiliating me, trying to pull me down off my pillar and back inside the illusory box, all because I wanted more from life than they may have wanted for themselves.

Come to think of it, all those incidents of bullying remind me of the parable of the crab that tries to climb out of a crowded bucket. Alone, the crab can easily get out. Its efforts, though, are undermined by the other crabs, pulling it back inside the bucket. But that pretty much sums up the story of my life—always trying to escape the bucket, only to get dragged back inside.

Finally, the light turns green. I put my foot on the gas pedal, only to slam on the brakes seconds later. There's an accident ahead, and traffic has come to a complete stop. "This just isn't going to be my day," I mumble of out frustration and slump back into the driver's seat.

Chapter Three

Much to my surprise, within minutes, two tow trucks arrive on the scene. The wrecked vehicles are promptly removed from the roadway, and traffic starts on its way. "Thank God for small miracles. I'm going to be on time after all," I say, heaving a sigh of relief as I tap the gas pedal.

Yeah, like I said earlier, I'm a dreaded lawyer—a scum-sucking P.I. attorney as some people call me. It used to bother me, people calling me a scum-sucker. These days I just laugh, as there could be worse ways to make a living.

I've practiced law for fourteen years now. Prior to graduating from law school, I clerked at some high-end, boutique law firms busting my ass, trying to land myself a position as an associate attorney. You know, one with all the perks—a friendly work environment, health insurance, a 401(k) plan, paid vacations, and respect, just a li'l bit of respect.

After my first year of law school at George Washington University, I clerked at the Republican National Committee in Washington, D.C. I landed that very sought-after position because I knew someone who knew someone with connections at the RNC. That's how things roll in the world of high-end Washington politics. It's all about connections.

My sole task that summer was to pull, copy, and brief every case ever decided in the entire United States on the issue of gerrymandering. The RNC wanted to redraw the voting district lines to disenfranchise minority voters. Because I did my job so well, the RNC offered me a full-time clerking position where I would work during the day and go to law school at night.

Looking back, I'm not proud of my accomplishments that summer, not at all. But in my defense, I was young and incredibly impressionable like those kids boarding the school bus this morning. Living inside a box, I did what I was told and never gave it a second thought. Shame on me, though. I really should have known better.

These days, I'm more of a free thinker—at least, when it comes to politics. I'm officially apolitical: as in, *I don't give a damn about politics.* I haven't belonged to a political party in years.

Anyway, everyone in that crazy town of D.C. was desperately climbing, trying to get to the top of the political pillar no matter the cost to their personal integrity. The atmosphere there was totally frenetic. Everyone was climbing over each other, on top of each other, whatever it took, even though no one had the slightest clue of what was actually at the top.

Let me tell ya. That's one pillar I decided to climb down from; and fast, I might add. I declined the RNC's offer and transferred to the University of Florida to finish law school. What a smart decision that was! I saved myself a boatload of money in student loans and preserved my personal integrity—and sanity—in the process.

Upon graduating from law school, I spent six years busting my ass, running a satellite office for a law firm where I became a partner after four years. At the age of thirty-two, I opened my own law firm with forty thousand dollars of capital, poster boards as signage, and folding tables and chairs. Now, I have six locations and bookshelves overflowing with open cases. A colleague once told me that my case load is really impressive, although it's hard for me to admit that to myself given my low self-esteem.

Day in, day out, I represent clients in all types of personal injury cases, laboring well into the late hours of the night. Last week, for instance, I rambled into the office one pitch-black morning at 4:00 a.m., so I could tackle the mile-high pile of documents on my desk. That's a fairly normal occurrence for me, by the way.

Clients desperately want money—as in yesterday—as though their P.I. settlement will be their life's saving grace. It baffles me; it truly does. But how did my clients live before crashing into someone's car?

Their desperation, though, can spell disaster for me. The threat of a client filing a complaint with the Florida Bar Association is always looming, dare I fail to live up to their expectations of hitting the legal lottery. So I really have no choice but to push myself to the point of exhaustion; or is it extinction?

Personal life? Me? Ha! Well, I really don't have one of those. I mean, when would I have the time for a personal life working eighty-plus hour weeks? Besides, my dating history is nothing short of disastrous, so I've taken myself off the market, absent occasional dating here and there. Although, secretly, I'm always looking around hoping to find "the one."

Since I'm valued and respected as a lawyer, that's where I focus my time and energy these days. People get in a car accident or slip on a banana peel at the local grocery store, and I'm one of the gazillion personal injury attorneys they can call upon (and do call upon) to get justice for themselves. Well, it's not justice, per se—just money. It's always about the moolah.

No matter what I do for my clients, all they're concerned about is the bottom line on the settlement distribution sheet—the compensation they expect me to get for them. And I'm good at getting the moolah for my clients—really, really good. "Aggressive" is what my phone book advertisements say, and that's my reputation or so I've been told.

One time, opposing counsel complimented me, saying I can turn chicken shit into chicken salad; meaning I can take the worse possible case and, through my hard work and talent, polish it and make it shine like a diamond. It's not a bad way to be thought of by one's peers, although I'd rather be known for something more public-spirited in nature. You know, like helping to usher in world peace or something along those lines.

The case that I'm arguing this morning is a bit different than my normal P.I. case and is definitely a hell of a lot more valuable than a helping of chicken salad. It's a high-ticket tobacco case. Mrs. Desuth smoked cigarettes ("death sticks" is what I call them) all her life and then surprise, surprise, surprise—she died of lung cancer.

"Not her fault," I argue whenever the defense attorneys point the finger of blame at her, attempting to sway the judge to rule in their favor. "It was the addictive nature of the nicotine that made her do it. The tobacco company knew that nicotine was addictive and hid this fact from her and millions of other users."

This case, by the way, has been assigned to the courtroom of the less-than-honorable Judge Joseph Smocket. What a royal prick he is. We went to the same high school, although he graduated decades before me.

Over the years, we've had our fair share of run-ins in the courtroom— like the time early on in my career when he called me "Miss Karis" through an entire summary judgment hearing while referring to opposing male counsel as "Attorney Taylor." Once he had ruled in my client's favor by denying the other party's motion, I courageously, yet very politely, called him out on his behavior. His reply, "When I started practicing law, Miss Karis, lady lawyers like you rarely existed. It's going to take me a while to get used to *your kind* being in my courtroom."

Astounded at what I heard, all I could do was shake my head, grab my briefcase and file, and accept there was no use arguing with him. But before I managed to escape, he added one more bit of insult (as if to rub it into my already battered self-esteem): "Miss Karis, I don't mean you any disrespect, but a young lady like you should consider finding herself a husband, having some kids, and settling down."

In today's world, it's hard to believe anyone (much less a judge) would even *think* that way, much less *make* such a comment publicly. But back then I just rolled my eyes (slightly, so as not to offend him) and headed for the door with my mouth closed shut, envisioning him grabbing me by my brunette locks and dragging me back to his cave to have his liberties with me.

That was back in the day when I walked into the courtroom wearing a jacket, skirt, silk blouse bearing just the right amount of cleavage, closed-toe high heels, and pantyhose that constricted me to the point of leaving seamlines embedded in my skin. In other words, I looked more like a Barbie doll, donning perfectly coiffed hair with fancy makeup and jewelry to match my outfit, instead of a hard-nosed litigator.

These days, it's pantsuits only—smart-looking, easy to move in, and putting me on an equal level with the male attorneys I go head to head with. My hair and makeup are more relaxed as well, displaying a look of carefree confidence, although I wish I felt as good about myself on the inside as I hope I look on the outside. Of course, it doesn't make a difference to Judge Smocket how I look or what I wear into his courtroom. His attitude toward me remains consistently the same—condescending.

Sure, I get that his wife doesn't work and his three daughters, while all college-educated, chose to be stay-at-home mommies. There's nothing wrong with that; but that doesn't mean all women want to take that path. I know I didn't when I was growing up and still don't—a husband, yes; kids, most likely, but I will never stop working—never. Working is in my blood; it's part of my ancestral lineage.

And that should be none of his concern anyway. My personal life, or lack thereof, is my business, not his. Ethically, he should be completely impartial when making his judicial rulings, but unbiased has never been in his repertoire, especially when it comes to me. For example, he was one of the concerned parents who, in my senior year of high school, came forward when a bomb threat was called in right before the graduation ceremony.

Let me tell ya. It was a whole crazy ordeal. I had been chosen to speak at the ceremony, along with a boy who I'd known since middle school.

Since I was only fourth in my class (the boy, my good friend, was third), I had never even expected to be chosen. But my high school, along with several others in the area, used a special committee system to select graduation speakers.

Well, my friend and I were chosen as speakers and that caused quite a bit of controversy because we were both Greek, and the valedictorian and salutatorian were both Jewish. The valedictorian and salutatorian felt the committee system was unfair, so the threat of an anti-Semitism lawsuit was made by them. It was followed by one, or maybe both of them (I can't remember specifics this many years later), writing a letter to our then President of the United States Ronald Reagan.

Then there was the trail of endless articles filling the local newspapers—everyone taking sides and stating their opinions on the matter with me in the spotlight once again, getting more humiliation that I didn't ask for. In the end, the school caved in and all four of us were allowed to speak with my friend and I being designated as guest speakers; and that was fine by me because I hadn't expected the honor anyway.

Unfortunately, it didn't end there. Some Greek boy wasn't pleased with the school's decision and called in a bomb threat right before the ceremony was about to begin. This forced the school administrators to cancel the event that night and reschedule for the next day. Boy, oh boy, were there a lot of upset students and parents.

Judge Smocket, a practicing attorney at the time, and whose youngest daughter was graduating along with me, stormed onto the field. He started pointing a finger at me while yelling, "It's all her fault."

"Like, what the fuck? Look at the evidence, you jerk. I didn't call in the bomb threat," I wanted to scream at him but held my tongue, out of respect for my elder.

Still, I can't believe he and a few more parents actually blamed me. It's ludicrous, but true, and incredibly hurtful to this day. I even got "booed" when I stood up to give my speech, but I took my licking and kept on ticking somehow managing to maintain composure. That's just a small sampling of the crazy shit I dealt with back in high school.

And now, bringing this whole damn thing full circle, Judge Smocket is the judge assigned to Mrs. Desuth's case. So here he is, once again, in a position of judging me. I really wish he would just recuse himself from the case, but that's never going to happen. He's doesn't possess that kind of judicial integrity; never has, never will.

So I guess I'm stuck dealing with this asshole, unless I find the courage to forcibly remove him by filing a motion for recusal. It's something I really need to ponder.

Chapter Four

It's five minutes and counting until I arrive at the courthouse. And besides worrying about where I'm going to park, I'm also seriously contemplating whether I should take the plunge and move to recuse Judge Smocket from the Desuth case. It's obvious from his past actions that he can't be impartial where I'm concerned, and the case is far too valuable for me not to consider doing it.

But moving to recuse him could be akin to a professional suicide mission. It might seal my fate on any future cases assigned to him and other judges who might get wind of my actions. That's just the way the judicial system works. Once you accuse a judge of bias, it can spell disaster for your legal career; not always, but it's a definite possibility.

So I will just have to tolerate his arrogance, the same way I tolerated all those arrogant bullies when I was growing up. It's chin up, move forward, and never ever let a bully see you sweat. That's how I dealt with the bullies back in school; and that's how I will deal with Judge Smocket, who I'm sure has been a bully his entire life.

Of course, because he's thirty years my senior, I didn't actually know Judge Smocket when he was growing up. Back in the day, he might have been a really nice guy. But I seriously doubt it because in my opinion, the old adage has truth: once a bully, always a bully. Leopard bullies don't change their spots.

In fact, I wasn't going to share this bit of information, but I will anyway. It's too late now to hold anything back. But when I found out that Judge

Smocket was assigned to the Desuth case, I did some investigating on him. I asked Joanne, a friend of mine who is a senior bureaucrat at the DMV, to do some digging. You know, find out what he's like outside the judicial realm.

After a couple of weeks, she texted me: "Let's have coffee, girlfriend. I've got news." We then met one morning, all cloak-and-dagger like, where she shared what all she had learned. And let's just say that a lot of it was less than flattering to Judge Smocket's reputation and to his marriage.

What I did by investigating Judge Smocket wasn't out of bounds, by the way. A smart personal injury lawyer always investigates the judges, the treating doctors, and the litany of expert and non-expert witnesses that pass through every case. Knowledge is key to successfully litigating a case, especially one as valuable as the Desuth case. I was just doing my job and doing it well.

Funny thing about judges, at least a lot of the older male judges, is that most of them have a bit of a shady past. They wouldn't want to have that past examined under a microscope.

One older judge, known for being a womanizer, actually asked me out early on in my career. I felt sick to my stomach when my assistant buzzed me to say he was on the line. Naturally, I presumed that I'd done something wrong at a hearing he'd presided over earlier in the day. Come to find out, he wanted to ask me out for dinner. What a relief that was, in a strange sort of way. At least I didn't screw up at the hearing.

Anyway, the legal community is tightknit. Lawyers talk. Judges talk. Even paralegals and assistants like to make a lawyer's business their business. And I didn't want to start my career off as the topic of lecherous snickers during a good ol' boys' golf game, so I politely and very professionally declined his offer. That's just the way—

My thoughts are interrupted, as I arrive at the courthouse. I pull into the metered parking lot, with just enough time to find a spot, park, and make it inside to the hearing. Some guy in front of me, though, can't figure out how to use the meter. "Hey, mister! Get a move on!" I yell, out my open car window.

Frustrated, I adjust my sunglasses, shake my hair, and look around to see if I recognize anyone's car. I don't, but I do notice the dirty orange sky in the distance, light effusing through chemically saturated smog and permeating a few clouds that blanket the horizon. It takes me to the thoughts I was having last night over a glass of chardonnay while I was stroking Barney, my soul cat, who was curled up in my lap.

If I get a really big verdict on this case, I'm quitting the practice of law, moving to Harbour Island in the Bahamas (with Picasso and my cats in tow), and becoming a writer. Forget about that dream of becoming a talk show host because I'd rather live out my days frolicking in the turquoise, blue waters of the Bahamas. Well, at least that's how I presently envision my dream life unfolding.

Chapter Five

"Desuth versus Southern Tobacco," I hear the court clerk cry out, her voice echoing across the courtroom.

The defense lawyers, an army of stiff gray suits, four in total, quickly rise and march in a single file line through the thigh-high, wooden gate dividing the judge's bench from the public gallery and take a seat at the table designated for the defense. Meanwhile, I struggle singlehandedly to gather my briefcase and large legal file which is partly strewn across the bench.

"Attorney Karis, will you be joining us today? Or should I summarily rule against your client?" Judge Smocket bellows out in his usual condescending tone.

"Yes, Your Honor. I mean, no, your Honor. My apologies." I shove the loose papers haphazardly into a red rope file and make my way through the gate and take a seat at the plaintiff's table located next to the jury box. Once I'm seated, I take a few minutes to organize documents I will be referring to during the hearing, making certain they are meticulously lined up on the table. I can't think clearly, otherwise.

Since my client (the representative for Mrs. Desuth's estate) is not required to be at hearing, I sit alone at the table. The suits sit at the other table, all paperless and bearing slim-lined laptops, never once cracking a smile. It's me versus Big Tobacco. Me versus the dark side. Li'l ol' me versus Goliath in a battle of good against evil where justice will be measured in dollar bills not blood.

Judge Smocket has his nose buried in his computer screen and is reading something. Perhaps, it's the lengthy response I filed to the motion being heard today. I spent the better part of three days writing it—thirty pages of sheer drudgery, case citations and all.

Sitting there, waiting on Judge Smocket, I think, *What I wouldn't give to simply escape this fricking profession and do something truly worthwhile. I don't just want to dish out P.I. settlements to money-grubbing clients for the rest of my life. Like my father, I want to build and leave a legacy. Maybe I will...*

Fidgeting in my chair, I tap my pen on a yellow legal pad, while my right leg shakes nervously under the table. *Focus, focus on the hearing,* I tell myself. *Right now, you must be a lawyer. Your dreams can wait.* The bailiff, who is standing to my left, gives me a sideways glance. Getting the hint, I put my pen down on the table.

By contrast, the suits could not be cooler. Between them, they are billing a collective three to four thousand dollars an hour. On the other hand, I'm working on a contingency fee basis, meaning I only get paid if, and when, my client gets paid. If the case tanks, all my time, effort, and costs incurred to litigate the case go down the drain—just like that!

Time is definitely on the side of the suits. Time makes them rich. Gawd, those guys are like something out of a *Zombie Apocalypse.* They've haven't flinched, not once, since sitting down at the table.

So why are we in this courtroom? Well, we're here because the suits have set a hearing on their motion to dismiss the complaint I filed on behalf of Mrs. Desuth's estate. It's a ridiculous motion, as the law is clear and in my favor on the issue addressed in the motion. But since the suits get paid by the hour, they file motions on every legal issue imaginable. Money, money, money—that's all the legal profession is about these days. It used to be a lot more noble (and ethical), until law schools started churning out more and more lawyers, and everyone jumped on the legal pillar.

When deciding the motion, Judge Smocket must assume that the allegations of the complaint I filed are true. To rule in favor of the suits, he must conclude that I failed to allege a valid claim on behalf of my client which is ridiculous. Hundreds of similar complaints have been filed against Big Tobacco, and mine is no different.

Finally, Judge Smocket looks up. He wriggles his nose, sniffs, and sneezes. I almost break out laughing because he's probably picked up the powerful scent of my Gucci perfume, which I'd sprayed while in the courthouse bathroom. "Well, Counsel," he states abruptly with no preceding niceties, "do you have anything new to add that has not already been eloquently set forth in the pleadings?"

Since it is Southern Tobacco's motion, the lead guy at the suits' table stands first. He cocks his chin, brushes a fleck from his suit, and regurgitates all the arguments that are in the written briefs. This is not notwithstanding Judge Smocket's request for anything *new*.

About ten minutes later—an eternity it feels like—he finally finishes. "Therefore," he says, "clearly there is no basis for an allegation of punitive damages" as we've set forth, ah, quite eloquently, as Your Honor has acknowledged, in our motion to dismiss the complaint. We kindly and humbly request that Your Honor, who is looking quite dapper today, grant our motion."

What a brownnoser! I think wanting to regurgitate something myself— my Diet Pepsi, that is. He is so obvious, so patently beseeching.

So what's this whole thing about in ordinary terms? Well, Southern Tobacco wants to avoid getting hit with millions of dollars in punitive damages for knowingly addicting millions of innocent victims to cigarettes which caused serious injuries and sometimes death. And this is all because it's hurting for profits. *Yeah, right!* I think, rolling my eyes facetiously.

"Attorney Karis, do you have something substantive to add?" Judge Smocket asks.

I stand and respond, "No, Your Honor. I rely on my previously filed response."

"Fine. In the future, I trust you will refrain from the use of facial gestures when you're in my courtroom."

"Yes, your Honor, sorry, I—" *Good grief.* I sit back down in my chair; and in a flash, the hearing is over. Judge Smocket firmly denies the defense's motion, and Team Karis wins!

And for a brief moment, I love Judge Smocket, really, really love him; and notwithstanding what I occasionally think out of frustration about the legal profession, I also love my clients and feel grateful for every single case that comes through my door. My feelings are short-lived, though, as I'm brought back to thoughts of how much I want to escape the legal profession. I've had enough of the insanity, and I'm totally burned out. For the past fourteen years, I've been mindlessly climbing this goddamn pillar with no end in sight. I desperately need to get down from it but don't know how to do it.

Sighing heavily, I glance over at the lead suit for the defense who is jabbering smugly, as if he just won the case. He and his minions suddenly break out in harmonic laughter as if the whole thing, including their loss, was comedic.

"You may have won today, Miss Karis, but you better be in this thing for the long haul," the lead suit says smugly. "Tee up, because now it will get serious."

"Sure thing," I reply smirking. "I've got my bat and ball ready to go."

Grabbing my briefcase and legal file off the table, I start to head out the gate but stop myself because I want to say something more to this guy. William Wright III—that's his name, but he goes by *Bill*—"as in the things that go in your money clip"—and is fond of joking in a very dry way. He's not that bad looking, really—square jaw, straight nose, a small but tasteful bald spot. In the right circumstances, I'd go out with him.

Hey, who knows? Maybe he is the one, as in my Prince Charming. I snort out a laugh at my internal joke. The fact I would even dare to contemplate Bill-like-the-things-that-go-in-your-money clip as being my Prince Charming is ludicrous. But given my crazy dating history, anything and anyone is theoretically possible.

Take for instance the guy who my hairdresser introduced me to a couple of years ago. He was hot, but Jeez-o-pete. During our one and only date, the guy blurted out that he believed all human life evolved from an invasion of alien lizards. That really killed the evening and any chance for a second date.

Then there was the Catholic priest I met at an outdoor wedding reception one hot, July afternoon. Somehow, he cajoled me into allowing him to draw my portrait as a gift for the bride and groom. Unbeknownst to me, he was drawing an erotic caricature of me. So two days pass, and he delivers it to my office along with a note inviting me to lunch. But that's not all. He also expressed a desire to explore a relationship with me. Of course, I politely declined both offers, not wanting to become the latest *National Enquirer* headline. Me, with a Catholic priest? Um, I don't think so.

Anyway, a girlfriend once encouraged me to write a book about all my dating tales. So one day, I decided to take her up on her suggestion. I mean, given some of my outlandish tales, why wouldn't I? It was sure to be a best seller.

In late 2000, I actually dove in and started outlining the series which I'd dubbed *The Toad Chronicles*, as in the girl who kisses too many frogs during her journey to find Prince Charming. Only in my series, everyone is a toad, full of warts and imperfections. I don't know exactly where the idea came from, really. It just sort of channeled through me one evening from somewhere. Maybe God has a sense of humor, after all.

Then in March of 2001, I started writing book one in earnest when I went to Harbour Island for a week-long vacation. I didn't get far with it, though. The tiny manuscript still sits in a folder in a desk drawer somewhere, patiently waiting for me to get back to my dream of becoming a writer.

One day, I'll get back to my dreams and hopefully, find my Prince Charming in the process. For now, I'm far too busy climbing this pillar that I'm currently on, dealing with the everyday grind of being a lawyer to consider doing anything else with my life.

Bill finally stops talking to his minions, looks at me, and asks, "Did you want something, Ms. Karis?"

"Not really. Well, yeah... I was just going to say that you're a toad in my new book."

"A toad? Excuse me?"

"Yes, you heard me, a toad."

"I beg your—"

"You're a toad who jabbers away and says absolutely nothing."

"What?... Hey, wait a minute...," he says.

I turn around, walk through the wooden gate, and head toward the courthouse exit. Once outside, I take a deep, long breath, feeling an enormous sense of relief for having survived another hearing with good ol' Judge Smocket.

Chapter Six

Having reached my car, I get inside and close the door. For some reason, I want to cry. A huge emotion is welling up inside me, taking my mind to my home away from home—Harbour Island. Something mysterious, otherworldly, Godly, drew me to the island years ago. It may have been the pink sand beaches I saw in a magazine one time, or it may have been something greater like a Divine calling.

My first trip to the island was March of 1999, a few weeks before I left the male-dominated firm where I worked and eventually became a partner. For six years, I ran the firm's satellite office in Tarpon Springs, building it from the ground up to over two hundred cases at the time I departed. I left, in a clandestine manner, and hung my own shingle down the street: The Karis Law Firm.

Why the departure? I'll tell you why—because one particular partner couldn't keep his dick in his pants, excuse my bluntness. And quite frankly, I'd had enough of his cavorting with my staff members. Mind you, he never got anywhere with me, despite chasing me around the desk several times. I became the first woman partner in that firm, a testament I believe to my never crossing the line with him.

Anyway, when I attempted to address the cavorting stuff at a partnership meeting one afternoon, I was told by my one partner (I'll call him "Bob") that our other partner's personal life was none of my goddamn business. Bob then threw a dig at me, saying that if I weren't an insecure woman none of what was going on would be a problem. Some nerve he had, saying that to me. He made me really mad; and I left the partnership meeting that day prepared to plot my departure from the firm.

A week later, I took my first trip to Harbour Island to rest up and gain clarity before making the big jump. While on the island my first night, there was a gas explosion in the kitchen of Valentine's Marina. I remember a huge shockwave going through my entire body, as I was jolted out of bed from a deep sleep. I ran out onto the balcony in my nightie, where I saw a massive ball of fire across the street.

The following day, I met an Englishman named "Peter," who had been raised in an orphanage as a child. At the age of fifteen, he joined the Merchant Marines (he had lied about his age to gain entry). Later, he became an enormous success in the shipping industry in north Africa. His personal story was so incredibly inspiring that it provided me with the courage to do what I should have done a few years earlier—leave my law partnership and never look back.

Recalling that fateful trip to Harbour Island, especially the explosion that first night, I know it was the start of my journey of coming out—not as a proud gay woman, as that's not me—but as an independent, empowered heterosexual female. It was a defining moment in my life, both personally and professionally.

If finances allowed for it, I would love to live on Harbour Island on and off throughout the year. I travel there every chance I get, escaping from the rat race and hoping to meet my Prince Charming. Fat chance, though. There's rarely a single man to be found on the island—well, other than Peter, who I met in 1999, but he was just a friend.

Still, I return to the island often, searching for what's missing within me. I only wish I knew what that something was. Lord knows, I've spent a small fortune trying to find it. It's as though I'm not complete, like the other half of my soul is out there somewhere searching for me, too. Everywhere I go, I find myself wondering if the next person I meet might be the one.

On a few occasions, I've thought I finally found the one, only to be wrong—painfully, painfully wrong. Most of the ones I've found or who have found me have been huge narcissists incapable of loving themselves much less loving me. Still, I go on searching.

My mother sees me searching, and she feels my pain because that's what mothers do—they feel their children's pain. Her solution is simple: find God. She tells me all the time, "Nikki, you need to believe and have faith in God."

It's not that I don't believe in God or have faith in Him, although my faith has been stronger in days past. I just can't swallow the mind-controlling propaganda spewed by organized religion that so many people buy into. Most people recite a bunch of Bible verses without ever truly knowing God through a direct, one-on-one experience (at least, that's how I perceive things); not that I've had a firsthand encounter with God, mind you. It's like they drank the Kool-Aid one morning at church and that was it. *Voilà!* God miraculously appeared to them, no questions asked.

Me, I want to feel and see God for myself, not just rely on what someone else has told me like a pastor, a preacher, or some other type of religious leader, who has probably never really felt or seen God either. And right now, I can't feel God, much less see Him, as he hasn't exactly been showing up for me these past several years.

Sure, from the outside, my life looks pretty damn good. I mean, I'm killing it in the personal injury legal market. Not only do I own a nice set of wheels, but I have a closet full of custom clothes and a home that will be a showplace once construction is finally complete. On the inside, though, my soul is dying a slow, painful death.

Not too long ago in late '05, I hit rock bottom after an abusive narcissist dragged me through the emotional swamp. A year later, and I'm still reeling from the experience, questioning why God delivered a total asshole to my doorstep.

The experience was a doozy, all right. Needing a break, I took a trip with my best friend at the time to the Four Seasons Hotel in Exuma. The night before our departure, I ate some bad sushi. Well, when we arrived at the Georgetown Airport, I was so sick that I could hardly stand. My friend, a hulking, woman with a head full of braids, scooped me up in one arm, our bags in the other, and somehow got me into a cab.

Well, three days later and ten pounds thinner, I finally emerged from the hotel room and joined my friend for lunch at the outdoor bar. Still queasy, I somehow managed to throw on a bikini, cover-up, straw hat, and pair of jeweled sandals and look semi-presentable.

Shortly after we sat down at the bar to eat, three tanned, handsome men sniffed an opportunity and approached us. One of them, let's call him "John," owned a huge yacht that was anchored out in the harbor. It wasn't long before he invited us aboard for dinner and drinks later that evening. And, well, my friend and I certainly weren't going to turn down an offer to climb aboard a yacht, especially since neither of us had ever seen one, up close and personal before.

That evening, everything started all light and lovely. We drank wine and had a long dinner where we all told our life stories. For John, especially, story-telling time was an opportunity for him to display his power, wealth, and rock-star lifestyle. But I had a few stories of my own to tell—like all the wonderful five-star resorts I had traveled to in the Bahamas and the Caribbean.

"You're lucky to have dated nice men who took you to all those places," Johnny said to me while filling my glass with a Merlot.

"Hardly, Johnny boy," I replied. "All those nice places—I paid for them myself from my hard-earned legal fees."

"You know, you need to meet my partner, Mitchell. He lives in Virginia but comes to Florida quite often for business. Mitchell likes independent women—me, not so much."

Before I could respond, John snatched his phone off the table, placed a call, and handed the phone to me with a chuckle. "Say hi to Mitchell," he said. Turns out Mitchell was the narcissist who later ripped my heart out.

After returning from Exuma, Mitchell and I started communicating several times a week. Two months into our exchange, he asked me if I wanted to meet him in New York City—a blind date of sorts. Mind you, the only picture I'd seen of Mitchell was one I'd found of him on the Internet from his brief foray in professional football in the mid-80's. But as crazy as the idea may have sounded, I was willing to take a huge leap of faith because it felt like destiny was drawing me in.

The first night I was in the City, we met for drinks at the rooftop bar of the Peninsula Hotel. When we locked eyes—*bam*! That was it. I knew I had found the one I'd been searching for. Not only was Mitchell good looking, but he felt intensely familiar. It's as if I'd known him my entire life. He finished my sentences, knew what to order me, and understood exactly what I was thinking. We were totally simpatico.

Once I was back home, though, Mitchell artfully began to pull me into his narcissistic web. During several tearful conversations, he revealed that he was going through a heated divorce with a custody battle involving his three children. He used this as a way of luring me into his wed, by confiding tales of sorrow about he and his children, and I was too blind by thoughts of him being *the one* to see what was happening.

Then when I was in way over my head, he upped the ante by promising to move to Florida to be with me. He also constantly bragged about all the wealthy people he rubbed elbows with, adding repeatedly that he came from a very wealthy family. The higher Mitchell piled all of this on, the more I gullibly swallowed what he was dishing out. And the result? I fell into a deep pit of insecurity, given my humble upbringing and fragile self-esteem.

By the time we finally parted ways, my self-esteem was shredded. Done. Finished. There was nothing left of it. And the worst part is that I allowed him to do it to me. In the end, he never even thanked me—just a "sorry, but I don't love you; see ya later, kid."

Even when he was gone, that wasn't the end of it. I got hooked on psychics for many months afterward, trying to understand what I had done wrong. So much money down the drain, seeking answers to what happened. And I still find myself getting pulled back into his web, especially when something prompts a memory of him.

Looking back, I should have seen the big, flashing neon sign: "Run for the hills!" But being in my late thirties, single, childless, and searching for the one, I ignored it all, especially since I loved his children and felt bad for them. My own lack of self-worth actually propped the asshole up on a pedestal—exactly what a narcissist wants a person to do. Gawd, I was so foolish! I still can't believe I fell for it all.

So now, as I sit in my car, I feel my tears pushing to be released; and they come, gushing out until my mascara has painted black stripes down my cheeks. When they stop, I'm exhausted, but I know what I must do. I need to figure out a way to get down from this goddamn pillar that I've mindlessly been climbing for so many years.

Chapter Seven

With a renewed sense of mission, I exit the parking lot and head south to meet with an orthopedic surgeon to prepare him for his deposition scheduled early next week. By the time I arrive at his office, I've reapplied my mascara and covered over my breakdown. Thankfully, there's no evidence of my prior disintegration, except for a bit of redness in my eyes.

The surgeon, a business acquaintance for the past ten years, performed surgery upon a client of mine a little over two years ago. Although my client's vehicle had suffered only minor damage in an accident, the jolt dislodged her prior cervical fusion which the surgeon then repaired. I meet with him for a little over an hour, going over all his notes and records, then grab a quick lunch at a nearby Italian delicatessen.

When I'm done, I head to the Don Cesar Hotel located on St. Petersburg Beach, a scenic, old hotel opened in 1928, at the height of the Gatsby Era. Thelma, my oldest niece, who is nine years younger than me, is getting married there tomorrow, a day I'm sure she will always remember. Family members and friends are flying in from around the country for what's guaranteed to be a breathtaking, outdoor ceremony.

I arrive at the hotel well before the posted time for check-in, but I'm in luck. The front desk allows me to check in early.

When I arrive at my room, I throw my bags onto the floor, then pour myself a glass of chardonnay and walk out onto the moon-shaped deck overlooking the beach. Standing on the deck, I realize how physically and mentally exhausted I am from climbing the pillar.

Since opening my law firm on April 19, 1999, I've been working day and night, usually seven days a week, trying to keep up with the demands of my burgeoning practice. It's no different than what I experienced in my partnership for six years, only this time the legal fees I earn are all mine. Thus far, I've been fortunate with my physical health holding up, although I know that I can only push the envelope so far.

Emotionally, I am also spent, having experienced way too many disappointments through the years. I have no idea how, or if, I will ever be able to fully recover from it all, especially after that horrible ordeal with Mitchell. The experience nearly destroyed me and, with it, any hope that I will one day find my Prince Charming.

And that's what a wedding is about, isn't it? It's the climax of the romantic story of a girl meeting her Prince Charming and being swept off her feet for a life filled with love, joy, romance, children, and holidays spent with family—all the things that are sublimely human. But here I am, not having yet experienced anything remotely close to that fairy tale—no husband, no children, no Christmas holidays spent cooking a turkey or decorating a tree—no one to share my thoughts, my dreams, and my hopes with, just empty, barren, and alone.

Aargh! I'm so angry with God right now. Why has He put me through so many painful ordeals? Why has He made me wait so long to find someone? Why has He delivered so many assholes to my doorstep? Why, why, why? I cast the remainder of the wine into the wind and head back inside my room.

The next day, the ceremony is held on the hotel's massive, outdoor marble staircase. Everyone, but the wedding party, is gathered on the grass below, sitting in plastic folding chairs, while the wind blows through their hair and music plays in the background.

As one of six bridesmaids, I have a bird's eye view of the ceremony. When Thelma enters the courtyard, she looks stunning in her wedding dress, and her fiancé looks drop-dead handsome in his black tux and tails. She has the biggest smile on her face. As Thelma speaks her wedding vows, I notice my lips mouthing them wishing I were her. I fight back more tears, not wanting to succumb to self-loathing or ruin photos of the wedding party.

Later that evening after dinner, all of us stand, raise our glasses, and toast to the bride and groom. After sitting back down, my cousin Mary Anne leans over and whispers, "I've been meaning to ask you. Are you still dating that guy from Virginia? His name was Mitchell, if I recall correctly."

"Yep, that's him. And no, we aren't dating any longer. Things didn't work out between us," I reply flatly, a huge wave of heartache washing over me. I think of telling her about the incredible grief I've endured and how it totally shattered me. But it's a wedding, and I don't want to ruin the positive vibes.

"There will be another," she says, grabbing onto my right hand and giving it a gentle squeeze.

I issue a hollow smile and reply, "Yes, you're right. And when it happens, I know it will follow the storyline of *Hope for the Flowers.*"

Mary Anne looks at me strangely. "*Hope for the Flowers*?" she asks.

"Yes, it's a book I was given as a high school graduation present," I reply. "Would you excuse me? I need some fresh air." I then stand and walk outside onto the verandah, leaving Mary Anne sitting at the table, alone.

Standing on the verandah, I look out onto the beach and watch the waves crash gently against the shore as a single tear rolls down my cheek. *Hope for the Flowers: that's my journey*, I reassure myself. *Whoever I am meant to be with in this lifetime, we will follow the storyline of that book.*

My mind wanders back to 1985, when I was graduating from high school, and a family friend gave me the book as a gift. Without reading a single page, I shelved it with the rest of my book collection. Over a decade later, when I was thirty, the book toppled from the shelf one afternoon and onto the tile floor of the family room. Still, to this day, I don't know how this happened because no one was home except me.

Believing it was a sign, I read the book that very day. I mean, how could I not? It practically jumped off the shelf at me. And what a huge impression it left. Given my love for the book, I ended up gifting dozens of copies of it through the years.

The author, Trina Paulus, tells the inspiring story of two caterpillars— Yellow, the female, and Stripe, the male. They meet as both are struggling to get to the top of a mythical pillar. Only instead of reaching the top, they become disillusioned and make their way back down the pillar, assisting each other on the way. Once they reach the bottom, they fall in love and start a life together living in the grass.

One day, though, Stripe feels disillusioned with his life and decides to start climbing up the pillar once again. Intuitively knowing she can't follow him, Yellow ventures off on her own, whereupon she meets an older caterpillar, spinning a cocoon. "Become a butterfly," he says. "Once you are able to fly, your life will be amazing. You'll see."

Initially, Yellow is reticent to take such a risk. But her reticence wanes, and she follows the elder's advice: she transforms into a beautiful, yellow butterfly.

Meanwhile, Stripe is ruthless in his resolve to make it to the top of the pillar. Then just as he's about to reach the top, he's distracted by the fluttering wings of a circling yellow butterfly whose eyes remind him of Yellow's. This smacks him hard, causing him to descend the pillar once again, whereupon he returns to the spot in the grass where he and Yellow fell in love.

Tired and heartbroken, he falls asleep, only to be awoken by none other than Yellow who is once again signaling him with her fluttering wings. This time, he is overwhelmed by the love he sees in her eyes. And then and there, a shift occurs within him.

Yellow patiently waits, while Stripe spins his cocoon and becomes a butterfly, too. Together, they fly off together to begin a new life. If only I could find someone who—

"Nikki," someone is saying, interrupting my thoughts. "Nikki, are you all right?"

I emerge from my daydream and see Mary Anne standing next to me with a worried look on her face. "Oh, gosh, I'm so sorry," I reply.

She smiles and extends a glass of wine to me. "It's a wedding, girl. Time to party and have some fun."

"You're so right," I say, grabbing the glass from her hand. We toast and both take a strong sip of wine, as the music starts to rise.

"Let's dance," she says, pulling me by the hand back inside the reception hall and out onto the dance floor. For the next several hours, she and I dance and dance and dance; and for the time being, I forget all of my troubles.

The next morning, with my head still abuzz from drinking the night before, I leap out of bed and pack my bags as I need to get to my office. Although it's a Sunday, I will be married to my desk, clearing off a mound of legal documents. Such is my life as a high-powered, personal injury attorney on the outside whose life on the inside is in complete shambles.

Chapter Eight

The hour-long drive home is sheer torture. I have way too much time to think, prompting my demons to surface once again. This is why I work so much; it helps to keep my mind occupied, so I avoid facing my demons and the root cause of my emotional pain.

I try to fend them off—my demons—but they persist and ultimately, they prevail. My mind slides backward to the self-deprecating thoughts I suffered over the weekend—being single, childless, loveless, and way, way overworked.

Emotionally, I'm also spinning from the mention of Mitchell's name at the reception. I want to break all ties with him, but his narcissistic claws are deeply imbedded in my heart. Gawd, I feel helpless—me, a woman who can bring defense counsel to their knees.

About halfway home, I hake Mitchell's grip by visualizing myself draped in heavy armor. I hammer thick iron nails into a medieval door behind which he is imprisoned, shutting him in and shutting myself out. Door successfully nailed shut. Finally, I'm free of his narcissistic grip and can move on.

I open the sunroof to the Rover. Relishing a rare day of low humidity in Florida, I take a deep, long breath. "There has to be more to life," I say to myself. "This cannot be all that there is, living this hellish nightmare."

My thoughts pivot to my childhood days before the crown of thorns and the hateful pins. Back in those days of innocence, I had such big dreams—meaningful ones—that could help better the world and make a positive difference in the lives of others. There was nothing I couldn't accomplish, if I put my mind to it, as I had so much enthusiasm for life and the energy to do it. All of the hardships I've endured through the years, though, have changed something in me. My inner spark is barely flickering, and my dreams are slowly dying.

Whenever I do somehow reignite the spark within me, I'm always pulled back inside the box or the bucket, whatever you wish to call it, by people or situations sabotaging me by screwing with my head. I don't get it—really, I don't. If only I could escape, I would then show everyone the way. Instead, I continue to feel like the lone crab, desperately wanting to escape the bucket, to be someone different, to do something different. But I feel stuck, more like trapped, and I don't know what to do about it.

My mother is always encouraging me to leap outside the bucket. "Go pursue your dreams, Nikki," she says. "God will help you make them a reality." She knows that I am meant to do something different with my life. What that is for sure, I cannot say.

When she was first pregnant with me, many people were aghast. She was forty-three years old when she gave birth to me and according to the town naysayers, far beyond child birthing years. Several people encouraged her to abort me, but she refused to cave to their pressure. Instead, she insisted: "This child is special. She is destined to do something important one day."

But now, here I am, doing nothing of the sort. I just wish I had my mother's courage. She has always been so very brave—a real trailblazer, the opposite of a conformist.

A few years ago, I did try to escape the bucket, as I wanted to be free to pursue my dream of becoming a published author and talk-show host. I had no idea exactly how any of that would transpire, but I did know that I needed a nest egg to protect myself financially. At age thirty-four, I had accumulated a sizeable chunk of money which I'd entrusted to a broker to conservatively invest. That was a huge mistake. In less than a year, the broker wiped me almost completely out. Most of my hard-earned money vanished with one margin call after another, until I pretty much had nothing left. My trust in the broker shattered, my stupidity in full bloom.

Traumatized that a large percentage of my financial security blanket was gone, something triggered in me. Investor psychosis set in, and I proceeded to lose even more money (what little I had left) by feverishly trading online, hoping to make back some of what I had lost.

Eventually, my dispute with the brokerage firm landed in arbitration, where I tried to recoup some of my losses. Let me tell ya. What a nightmare that turned out to be! Being the client and not the attorney was a huge eye-opener for me.

Anyway, long story short, I ended up settling with the brokerage firm in the middle of the arbitration proceeding. Even though I only collected pennies on the dollar, I felt proud for sticking it out. It's not always about the money; sometimes, it's about the principle.

After this financial devastation, though, something creative miraculously opened up inside me. That's when I birthed the concept for *The Toad Chronicles* series. It channeled to me straight from God, the Universe, or whatever you wish to call it, as it wasn't something that emerged from my conscious thoughts.

Moved by something deep and spiritual, I feverishly jotted my ideas down on paper. The inspiration, though, died as quickly as it had arisen. That's when I put my ideas into a folder and stashed them away in a drawer. I thought I needed—

My cellphone rings, interrupting my thoughts. It's Clare, my paralegal. "Hey, Nikki! I'm dying to know. How was the wedding?"

"Lots to tell you. Are you free right now? I'm on my way home."

"Sure, sure, I'm at the nail salon getting a manicure and pedicure. Come meet me here."

"Great, I'll be there shortly."

Then after I hang up with Clare, the metaphoric iron nails pop out of the medieval door. And I'll be damned, if Mitchell doesn't leap back into my consciousness. I'm drawn back to Harbour Island, the week of Valentine's Day 2005, when he and I took a trip there together. It was only the second or third time I had spent Valentine's Day with someone, a sad testament to my relationship history.

Suffice it to say, the getaway ended up being a total disaster. By the time I arrived back home, my already fragile self-esteem had sunk to a new low. Not to mention, I got stiffed with a huge hotel bill. And now, this very same asshole is invading my head once again.

You know, if I don't learn to love myself again and rebuild my self-esteem, I will never shake Mitchell and the rest of the narcissists permanently from my life. It's something I really need to work on.

Chapter Nine

"Hey, stop rubbernecking!" I yell out the window of the Rover. I'm frustrated because the cars in front of me have slowed to a crawl to catch a glimpse of some car accident. This is why I stay so busy in my law practice; it's the fifth or sixth accident I've seen in the past three days.

Traffic finally starts moving, and I turn into the nearest parking lot where the nail salon is located. With all this delay, I wonder if Clare will still be at the salon. I realize, though, that I didn't ask her exactly *which* salon she is at. She may be at the one across the street as this place, while her favorite, is too expensive except for special occasions.

Whoa! I slam on the brakes. As crazy as it sounds, there's a large dog lying in the middle of the parking lot.

I throw the Rover into park, jump out, and race over to the dog, joined by two other people seeing the same odd thing I am. One is a woman, who says she gave the dog a hamburger to eat when she first entered the parking lot; the other is an older man driving a white truck.

The dog is male, mostly brown in coloring with a smattering of white on his chest and paws, and he has the most wretched, awful stench about him. I mean, it's enough to make me want to gag, and I'm standing five feet away from him. From the looks of things, he appears to be injured, although I'm not sure what is wrong with him.

"Can you help me get him into the back of my car? I'll take him to the emergency vet," I say to the man and woman, wondering if the stench will stain the Rover.

"Absolutely," the woman replies.

The older man then says, "Hold on, young lady. I have a sheet and some rope in my truck. Let me get them. I don't want you ruining this beautiful set of wheels."

While he's off searching through his truck, out of the corner of my eye, I see another man, with a head full of white hair and a stark white goatee, riding toward us on a bicycle. It has a basket on the front of it like Dorothy's bicycle in *The Wizard of Oz*.

As he gently stops the bicycle a short distance away, his shirt causes me to do a double-take. He's wearing a tattered white t-shirt with the cover of *Hope for the Flowers* printed on the front of it. I blink a few times, stunned by the serendipity of what I'm witnessing, and think, *I must be imagining this, as it just can't be real. Last night, I was telling Mary Anne about this very book.*

Wide-eyed, I walk over to the man and say, "Wherever did you get that shirt? That's my absolute favorite book."

He replies, "I know."

What? How could he know? I've never met or seen this man before today, I think, bewildered by this encounter.

Suddenly, I'm hit with an overwhelming force. Tears start streaming down my cheeks, and my whole body begins to shake. Something totally amazing is taking place right now, although I have no idea what it is or where it's coming from.

In shock, I don't say another word to the man. Instead, I turn around and return to the injured dog, who is still laying on the pavement unable to move. The man in the truck ties the rope around the dog's neck as a makeshift lead while the woman wraps the sheet around him.

Together, the three of us load the sickly creature into the back of the Rover. All the while, the prescient man watches us intently from a short distance away.

After the dog is loaded, and I thank the man and woman for their assistance, I climb back into the driver's seat. I resolve to follow the man with the bicycle, sensing he is the leader, and I am meant to follow him. Wobbling through the parking lot on his bicycle, he slows at the stop sign, then proceeds through. I stop at the sign and look both ways; but when I look back, *poof!* The man on the bicycle has vanished.

"Holy shit!" I exclaim, totally flabbergasted by what just occurred. I sit there for a few minutes, shaking my head feeling very much confused, then call Clare and relay what just happened.

"I think he was an apparition," she says. "I've read about that kind of stuff."

"Whatever he was, I'm pretty freaked out by it, but I've got to run. I need to get this dog to a vet. I'll see you in the morning."

Fifteen minutes later, I arrive at an emergency veterinarian clinic and park near the entrance. The dog cannot walk, so I ask the girl at the front desk to assist me in getting him inside. Together, we lift him out of the back of the Rover, a Herculean task given his size. We then bring him inside the waiting room, where we lay him down on the floor.

As I sit near him filling out some paperwork, I inhale a smell that turns my stomach. It's the stench from him, now reeking from my hair and clothing. I pinch my nose, trying to block the smell, but my efforts prove futile.

Eventually, the vet tech comes out; and miraculously, the dog leaps to his feet, although he is favoring his back right leg. The vet tech slips a lead around his neck and says, "You need to prepare yourself. Your dog appears to have a broken hip and a flesh-eating skin disease."

She then departs with him toward the back of the clinic. Meanwhile I sit in the lobby, thinking of the exorbitant vet bill that I'm about to incur. I also worry the flesh-eating disease might be contagious, and that I might require medical treatment myself.

A tad on edge, I grab a magazine and place it on my lap, thinking I'll flip through the latest vacation offers. But before I can do anything, the pages fall open to an article featuring Mitchell's children. My breath catches in my throat as I think: *There is absolutely no way this just happened. What are the odds?*

And I'll be damned, if that medieval door doesn't pop open again, allowing thoughts of Mitchell to flood my consciousness. My heart flutters, and I'm thinking this must be some sort of sign. The prescient man led me here, to this very point in a Universe full of trillions of possibilities.

Holy cow! This is so amazing, I think, my head hunched forward, scanning every word. And when I'm done, I sit there daydreaming about Mitchell and his children until the vet comes out.

"It appears your dog is a big sissy," the vet says after introducing herself.

"A sissy?"

"Yes, his hip is okay. All he has is a broken, non-weight-bearing toe. Apparently, he was just seeking some attention today."

"And what about the flesh-eating disease, the stench?" I ask.

"Oh, that? He rolled in some roadkill," she chuckles. "But I do have concerns about his behavior. He's not your dog, right?"

"No, he's not. I found him in a parking lot. I couldn't just leave him there injured and all alone."

"Of course not. I'm not suggesting that you would."

"What kind of dog is he?" I ask out of curiosity, although not knowing much about dog breeds.

"Well, if I had to guess, I'd say a boxer-hound mix," she replies, then says, "Look, I want to relay to you that he has some cautionary yellow flags. Things that might be problematic behavior-wise."

"What do you mean?" I ask, trying to get a better understanding.

"Um, well, it's kind of hard to describe. It's a look in his eyes that I've seen doing what I do. You've owned a dog before, right?"

"Actually, no, I haven't. I've had several cats through the years but never a dog. And my house, it's under major renovation right now, but I'm sure I'll figure things out."

"I'm sorry to tell you this, if you had your hopes on him. I'd strongly advise that you relinquish him to the Humane Society. They'll either adopt him out or find him a rescue," she says.

"Um, well, I—"

"Caroline!" she yells, cutting me short. "Can you please give Miss, ah..."

"Karis, Nikki Karis," I say.

"...Ms. Karis the form for the Humane Society." Then turning to me she adds, "Even though he's not your dog, you did find him and what's the saying? 'Possession is—'"

"Nine-tenths of the law," I finish for her, and we both laugh.

"Yes, and again, it's customary that we have the person who brings an animal in to authorize release to the Humane Society. Is that okay?"

I hesitate, because the dog is really tugging at my heartstrings. But since I've never owned a dog before, I'm nervous I won't be able to handle him based upon what the vet is telling me.

"He'll be okay there?" I ask.

"Of course. We send many animals there. It's what they do."

Caroline reappears with a clipboard and dangling pen. I take the pen and hesitate for a moment. "This is the best thing for you and the dog," the vet says in an urging way.

I reluctantly sign on the dotted line and hand the clipboard back to Caroline. "So that's it?" I ask.

"Yes," Caroline replies. "Would you like to say goodbye to him?"

"Uh, sure, why not?"

The vet disappears down the hallway to help the next animal in distress, and Caroline shows me to the area where "my" dog is being held. He looks peaceful but somber, unaware (presumably) of his fate.

"Goodbye, big guy. Thanks for being a part of my journey," I say as he gives me a sad-eyed look complete with ears twitching sullenly.

Caroline then opens the door to the kennel he is in, allowing me to pet him. Tearing up with emotion, I caress his ears and give him an all-over-body rub down, then quickly close the door.

After paying the bill, totaling a whopping eight hundred dollars, I leave the clinic, sensing that I'm pushing against a tremendous force of fate. I'm also feeling badly that I've surrendered him because it's not like me to give up on anyone or anything quite so easily.

Walking through the parking lot toward the Rover, it all starts to hit me, and I get choked up with emotion. "I just can't bring him home to live with me right now," I argue to myself. "The house is in the chaotic throes of major construction; and I can't install a fence to contain him, not until more of the project gets done. It just wouldn't work out."

I hop inside the Rover, wipe away a few tears that have escaped, and head straight for home.

Chapter Ten

Twenty minutes later, I pull into the portico of my home, feeling a huge mountain of regret, having signed Paulie (the name I've given to him) over to the Humane Society. Once inside the house, and knowing what I must do, I find the vet's card in my bag and call the clinic.

"Hi, Caroline, it's Nikki Karis. I'd like to get Paulie back," I say.

After a long pause, "Excuse me?"

"The dog, I named him Paulie after Trina Paulus, the author of *Hope for the Flowers*. The guy on the bike... Look, it doesn't matter. I just want to bring him home. I need him as much as he needs me."

"Oh my, Nikki, well, I'm sorry, but he's already gone to the Humane Society."

"Uh—" I find this hard to believe because I just left the vet's office, and the Humane Society is located some thirty minutes away. "You're sure he's already gone?"

"Yes, he's gone," she replies. "He's now in their possession. They don't open until tomorrow morning."

I hang up the call with gritted teeth and determination. There is absolutely no way I'm giving up on getting Paulie back, even if it means taking legal action to get him. He is meant to be with me; he is a part of my journey. I feel it in every fiber of my being.

That night, I don't sleep but a few winks, worried about his fate.

The next morning, I google the number for the local Humane Society and call them. A woman answers the phone, and I relay to her that I'm interested in the hound-boxer mix, brought in from the emergency clinic in Palm Harbor the day before. Caroline told me the truth, as the woman confirms that Paulie arrived there yesterday afternoon.

But when I request to have him back, I get hit with the second punch to my gut. "Ma'am, I'm afraid we can't do that. He has some cautionary yellow flags. We will only be able to release him to an approved rescue person. Are you approved?" she asks.

"No, but that's ridiculous. I'm the one who found him. I didn't have to give him up to begin with. The vet's office pressured me, so—"

"I'm sorry, Mrs.—"

"*Ms.* Karis, and I'm an attorney, ma'am. I'm going to drive to your facility right now. If you don't give me Paulie back, you will see a lawsuit on your desk before the day is over." I hang up the call, immediately get into the Rover, and drive to the Humane Society. I'm afraid they're going to ship Paulie off to God knows where or give him away to someone else before I arrive. Then what will I do?

Twenty-five minutes later, lucky to not have gotten a speeding ticket, I pull to a screech in the Humane Society parking lot and storm inside. I don't even give the receptionist a chance to talk because I immediately chime in with: "Please tell the head administrator that I'm here to see him or her about getting my dog back, the boxer mix that arrived yesterday afternoon. I called not too long ago."

The receptionist disappears into the back and out comes a woman, bearing a huge smile. "Hi, I'm Susan, the head honcho here. I was just about to call you," she says.

She's trying to be pleasant, I can tell, but I suspect her motive is to convince me to leave without Paulie. But if there's one thing you never want to do, it's piss off a litigation lawyer—in particular, a litigation lawyer who is on a mission. And I'm not leaving, under any circumstances, not without my Paulie.

"Nice to meet you," I say, trying to be cordial. "I'm here to get my dog back."

"Well, please, follow me to my office. Let's talk about it," she says, before escorting me back to her office.

Once inside her office, I sit opposite her at her desk. It's a soulless office, I notice, with no family pictures or soothing effects whatever. Being that it's very bureaucratic looking, I brace myself for anticipated obstinance but much to my surprise, that's not what happens. Instead, she tells me she's heard really good things about me through the community, as she actually lives in the Tarpon Springs area.

"You know, I'm not supposed to do this since you aren't an approved rescue. But since I know you're responsible and will take good care of the dog, I'm going to bend the rules this one time," she says, reaching inside a desk drawer.

Then without any further ado, she takes out some forms and tells me to sign them. She is happy to return Paulie to me, although she does warn me that he will be a lot of work. Thinking she's just biased because he's not a purebred, I graciously thank her for her concern. And in one stroke of the pen, he's officially mine once again.

The next thing I know, he's riding in the back seat of the Rover as we head toward home with his snout hanging blissfully out the window. *He is so damn cute. I'm so happy I got him back. I've really made the right decision here*, I think, watching him revel in the wind.

When we arrive home, I open the door to the Rover and grab him by the leash. Immediately, he begins pulling me, wanting to sniff everything in sight. I notice that he's incredibly strong, and it takes all my strength to control him.

Taking him by the leash, I show him around the recreation room (more like, he leads the way), which is where he will be living since the main house is under construction.

Then as I walk him around to the front lawn (again, he leads the way), *boom!* He bolts, jerking the leash out of my hand.

"Pauulieeeee!" I yell at the top of my lungs. But it's too late because he's already scurrying down the street like he's outrunning aliens. My heart races, worried he'll be hit by a car.

"Please, help! Can you try to catch him?" I say in a panic to the two painters, who are working at my house.

"Yes, yes," one of the painters replies, taking off with a wet brush in hand, while the other painter isn't far behind him, pumping his knees like an Olympic sprinter—a comical scene, as you might imagine.

Meanwhile, I make a mad dash toward the back of the house. I grab my car keys, jump in the Rover, and floor it after them.

Thankfully, the painters catch Paulie several blocks away and bear hug him until I arrive. He's safe, although covered in a few white brush strokes. And the painters, while winded, are proud of their accomplishment.

"Hey, big guy, why did you run from me?" I ask Paulie as though he's going to answer me.

I take him by the leash, while the painters head back toward the house. He jumps into the back seat of the Rover and turns his head away from me, looking quite perturbed. Obviously, he's displeased that he's been so easily captured.

Chapter Eleven

After arriving home, Paulie heads straight to the couch in the recreation room and falls fast asleep. I stroke his head and kiss his face, but he doesn't respond. I'm completely crushed. Day one of dog ownership, and I've been royally dissed by my pooch.

He just needs time to settle in and get used to his surroundings, I think, stuffing a blanket under his head to make him comfortable. I'm hopeful tomorrow will be a better day and the day after that one even better.

The next morning, I call my office and ask Clare to free up my day and route all of my phone conferences to my cellphone. It's Paulie's first full day home, and I want to spend time acclimating him to his new surroundings.

Thankfully, he's a lot more cooperative today than he was yesterday, allowing me to take him for short walks around the property without pulling me down. While I speak with clients and review a stack of files, he snoozes away on the couch, waking from time to time to watch episodes of Animal Planet playing on the big screen TV.

The following morning, after getting dressed and taking Paulie for a short walk, I load him into the Rover. I've decided it's time for him to meet Clare and my other assistants. My calendar is fairly light for the day, so it's the perfect time to get him adjusted to the office.

"Oh, gosh, you're a handsome devil," Clare says to Paulie as we burst into the lobby. Before you know it, she's petting him lavishly, while he laps up the attention. At one point, he lays down on the tile floor and rolls over onto his back, and she scratches his belly. I stand there, allowing the two of them to establish their bond.

"All right, all right, enough already. Don't give him a big head. I've had enough narcissists to last a lifetime," I say to Clare, letting out a chuckle.

"Are you sure you can handle him? He's a pretty big dog. Maybe you should consider finding him another home." Paulie immediately sits up and cocks his head to one side. He looks at me, like he understands what Clare just said.

"Of course, I can handle him. I mean, come on. I handle those nasty defense lawyers, don't I? I'm sure I can handle *a dog*."

"Okay, but I've had dogs before, and this one seems to have a lot of issues with his running and all."

"We all have issues, Clare. Dogs are no different than humans. It's unfair for you and everyone else to judge him. Give him a break. He's been through a lot," Paulie lets out a single, loud bark, apparently happy that I've stood my ground with Clare.

I grab his leash and lead him back to my office to do some work. As we're walking down the hallway, I say to Paulie, "I better watch what I say from now on. You apparently speak humanese."

About an hour later, one of my assistants runs to the post office and fails to tightly close the front door on her way out. Paulie, who has been lying in the hallway, gets wind of the partially open door. The next thing I know, he scrambles to his feet and darts out the door, soon racing perilously down the busy street.

I scream his name, as I race out the door after him in my high-heeled booties, jeans, and sweater with three of my staff members tight behind me. The road is thick with traffic. Any sane person would think he was on a suicide mission.

"This damn dog is going to give me a heart attack," I huff to myself, watching him dart between cars that have now stopped for a red light. I make a mental note to up my workout routine now that Paulie is around. He's a runner!

A few seconds later, a woman pulls her car onto the shoulder a few feet behind me. She yells out her car window, "Hey, that's my dog!"

"Your dog?" I yell back in astonishment, stopping dead in my tracks.

"Yeah, he jumped out of our apartment window Saturday night."

I immediately get into her car. Together, we follow Paulie on his suicide mission down the busy street, cringing every time he almost gets sucked under the wheel well of a car. Thankfully, a man in a pickup truck sees what is happening and pulls up next to us on the shoulder.

"Does he like pickup trucks?" he yells out the open driver's window.

"No clue," I reply.

The man speeds ahead of us along the shoulder, until he pulls to a stop about five hundred yards away. He opens the driver's door and coaxes Paulie inside. My comrade and I follow the man to the nearest parking lot with my assistants, breathless, trailing behind us. When we arrive at the lot, Paulie is sitting in the front seat of the truck, breathing heavily, his tongue hanging down.

"Thank you so much. You were a lifesaver," I say to the man.

"You're welcome, ma'am," he says as I grab Paulie's leash from one of my assistants and clip it onto his collar. Paulie jumps out of the truck, and the man drives off with a wave.

"I can't thank you enough for rescuing Deuce," the woman says to me. "My husband and I sold our house and moved into an apartment a few months ago. Because he's so miserable being locked up all day, he always tries to escape. He's done it several times already."

"Well, just to be certain that Paulie, I mean Deuce, is actually yours, can you tell me what color collar he was wearing when I found him?"

She confirms the collar was green. That, together with a few other things, convinces me she is, indeed, his legal owner. I reluctantly hand her the leash, and she hands me one of her business cards. Paulie then hops into the back seat of her car, and they take off, his head hanging out the back window.

"How could you just let Paulie go like that?" Clare asks me once they have departed. "You love him so much."

"I know I do, but she's the legal owner," I say as tears well up in my eyes. "Mark my words, though. Paulie will escape again and be back to me within the next six months. He has microchipped my name into his conscience."

Walking back to the office, I fight back my tears, trying to convince myself that losing Paulie is no big deal. "It's just a dog," I repeat several times to myself.

Once we're back at the office, I sit down at my desk, thinking about all the serendipitous events that have occurred since Paulie first entered my life—the man on the bike, the cover of *Hope for the Flowers* on his t-shirt, the magazine article about Mitchell's children, and now his owner miraculously appearing on the scene. It all seems so bizarre, and I'm grappling to understand the meaning of it—to put the pieces of the spiritual puzzle together.

One thing is for certain—the serendipity of it has shaken me at my core and awakened something inside of me, although I don't exactly know what that may be. What I do know is that the pillar I'm currently climbing is feeling more ominous than ever.

"Nikki, are you all right?" Clare asks, sticking her head into the door and checking on me like she always does.

"Yes, I'm fine. I'm just thinking about Paulie. That dog and I are so connected. I know there is more to our journey." She looks at me, nodding in agreement.

I start crying, always quick to wipe away the tears. "I also think Mitchell will be back, only this time transformed, like Stripe in *Hope for the Flowers*. He will see the light and share my vision of helping to empower others."

"Oh, God, not Mitchell. That narcissist has caused you too much pain. Most people never transform, and he's certainly not going to be the exception to that rule. He's way too self-centered."

"Well, I thought the same thing until Sunday when I found Paulie. The whole experience has given me hope again that Mitchell will transform and become my Stripe. Now, let's get back to work."

I turn my attention to the huge mound of legal documents sitting atop my desk. Staring at it, I realize it's going to be another late, lonely night at the office, and even lonelier when I go home without Paulie by my side. Sighing heavily, I dive in.

Chapter Twelve

It's now 5:00 a.m., January 30, 2007, and today I turn the big 4-0. Paulie is still with his owner, and I am not only dogless but spouseless, childless, and pretty much alone in my life.

I put my pen down on the desk and close my eyes, allowing my thoughts to wander to the day I graduated from law school. At the time, I was twenty-five years old, starry-eyed, and ready to take on the world. Since that momentous day, I've single-handedly built a personal injury law practice that spans five counties. Yet, despite my outward success, I feel emotionally empty inside.

Although I've longed to find my Stripe, I have so far only met toads on my journey, one right after another...hoppity hippity hop. But I remain resolute about my belief that my Stripe, whomever he may be, will share my vision of building something together to help empower others.

That's the kind of man I'm searching for—a man with a vision, a philanthropic man like my father—and I won't settle for anything or anyone less.

When noontime rolls around, Clare steps into my office with a giggle. "Are you ready for your birthday lunch?" she asks.

I roll my eyes and say, "Sure, meet you outside in a few minutes."

Today's birthday celebration will be simple, nothing extravagant— lunch at a local Italian restaurant with my mother, father, and assistants, since my inner circle is incredibly small these days. It's safer that way because many of my girlfriends have turned against me through the years.

I'm not perfect, by any means. But some of the stuff that's been done to me, both personally and professionally, has been downright shitty. Life lessons, I'm sure, but incredibly painful, nevertheless.

Just six months ago, my best friend, Marlene, who I'd known since college, became the latest statistic. She's the girlfriend who was with me in Exuma. Shortly before she jumped ship on our friend*ship*, I went solo to the Four Seasons in Punta Mita, Mexico. At the time, I was completely exhausted from working long hours, seven days a week. I was also still reeling from the narcissistic aftereffects of Mitchell.

The day after I arrived in Mexico, my mother called and said, "Your father's had a severe gallbladder attack. He's undergoing surgery in a couple of hours. The doctor is concerned that he might not make it."

"Not make it? What do you mean?"

"Honey, I have to go. The doctor is signaling that he wants to talk to me. I'll call you when the surgery is done."

After she hung up the call, I threw myself onto the king-size bed and shouted, "I'm so angry with You, God. Why do You continue to forsake me?" I cried for hours, waiting for news of my father's condition. Finally, my mother called; thankfully, my father made it through surgery, alive.

The next morning, I emailed Marlene in hopes of getting some comfort and support. With my world spinning, I told her that I was in a really dark place between the demands of my law practice, the heartbreak with Mitchell, and my father's ailing health. I also expressed that I was angry with God. "What am I to do?" I wrote her.

But instead of lending a sympathetic ear, she made the situation about her by writing: "You know I don't like it when you get angry with God." She then proceeded to lecture me about a number of things, when all I wanted (and needed) was some emotional support.

That's when a lightbulb turned on in my head, and I realized our friendship had pretty much been a one-way street—me giving, her taking, and rarely the other way around. I had gone above and beyond to help her through the years and the one time when I really needed her support, she wasn't there for me.

That's the way I perceive so many of my relationships going down through the years, with both men and women alike. As long as I was giving to the other party, things between us were great. But the minute I stopped giving and needed something for myself, well—

"Nikki," Clare says, interrupting my thoughts. "We're waiting."

"Yes, sorry, I got sidetracked," I say, grabbing my bag and following her out the door.

When we arrive at the restaurant, my parents are already there, sitting at a table. My mother is so amazing. She turned eighty-three last month and is still going strong, working both in my law office and in real estate, while caring for my father. How she manages to do it all while looking and dressing impeccably is beyond me.

I plop down in a chair next to my father and kiss him on the cheek. "How ya feeling today, Pops?" I ask him.

"Not too good, baby. I hurt all over," he replies with a look of pain in his eyes. "My shoulders and knees are killing me, and I can barely move these hands of mine." He holds them up and squeezes them. I notice both are swollen—inflammation from osteoarthritis and all the medications he is taking.

"Well, tomorrow will be a better day," I reply, rubbing his hands before turning my face away from him so he can't see me tearing up.

My father, Nick (whom I'm named after), is eighty-seven years old. For the past two decades, he's suffered with one ailment after another. Most of them started after an automobile accident, when a young man plowed into the back of his work truck. Yet somehow, despite his physical aches and pains, he's managed to maintain a positive outlook, always extending a helping hand to anyone in need.

Every day, he makes his rounds around town, visiting various stops and sharing his tales of the history of Tarpon Springs and the families who founded it. If someone mentions needing something, well, my father is always willing to pitch in and help them. Giving to others has been therapeutic for him, lifting his spirits and keeping him going. Recently, though, his positive spirit has begun to wane.

As I observe him today, he looks tired, like he's ready to leave for another realm. I push this painful thought away, although deep down I sense that my father's physical time on Earth is nearing an end.

Chapter Thirteen

Three weeks later, on February 16th, the instincts I had during my birthday lunch prove accurate. My father is whisked by ambulance to the emergency room, after having had a heart attack at home.

A few hours earlier, he had been released from another hospital, having had breathing problems related to congestive heart failure. At the time of his release, the doctor ordered him on assisted oxygen. That, along with the thought of being in a nursing home (not that my mother would have put him in one), must have totally freaked him out. No doubt, this stress caused or contributed to his current heart attack.

I arrive at the hospital as fast as I can and meet my mother outside. "Your dad has suffered a massive heart attack. The doctor doesn't expect him to survive the night," she says, before rushing back inside of the emergency room.

What? No! This can't be true! I think, standing in the parking lot alone, dry heaving uncontrollably. I try to process my mother's existential words but can't as the situation is way too overwhelming.

"Please, God, don't take him. I need him, I need him," I say, dropping my knees down onto the pavement and cupping my hands over my face. "I beg of You, God, not now. Please, not now."

Finally, I pick myself up, gather my courage, and head into the emergency ward. Several of my family members are already bedside, as the doctor tends to my father. While everyone is busy talking with each other, I see my father rise up out of the bed and pull his oxygen mask off. He looks me straight in the eyes and says, "I'm coming back," before lying back down.

I yell out, "Hey, did anyone see that?" but everyone ignores me as though actors in another scene. It's like my father and I, and only my father and I, co-exist on a different plane in another dimension. My heart leaps as I think: *My father is going to make it. He is so incredibly strong. If anyone can do it, he can.*

Defying the doctor's prognosis, my father lives through the night. The next day, my nieces and nephew, who have flown in from around the country, come by the hospital to see him. He is cognizant and able to talk with them, but he and I don't speak to each other. It's like we're both afraid that if we do speak, it will be our last conversation.

That night, I stay with him in CCU, attempting to sleep on an uncomfortable chair. Although he seems unconscious from the morphine the doctor has given him, I stroke his face and talk to him, assuring him how much he is loved, while Linda, his nurse, comes into the room from time to time to check on him. Occasionally, she grabs his hands and rubs them gently while saying, "My Nicky, you're going to be all right."

Sadly, as the night goes on, his vital statistics slowly decline. The only words I hear him utter are, "Baby, I'm tired. I can't go on."

I don't want to see my father suffer any longer, so I courageously say to him (even though it's absolutely killing me), "You can go now, Pops. I'll be all right. Promise."

Given our incredibly tight bond, I know that I'm the one who needs to let him go. I'm his baby, the one he's measured the latter stage of his life. At his 80th birthday party, I roasted him about it, recalling how he promised to keep on living until I accomplished certain milestones in my life.

During my senior year of high school, he started by saying: "I'm going to live to see my daughter, Nikki, graduate from high school." Then it was seeing me graduate from college. A few years later, he said: "I'm going to live to see her graduate from law school." In my late twenties, he progressed to: "I'm going to live to see Nikki open her own law firm."

And, well, just about the only milestone I haven't yet achieved in my life is getting married, so I joke that my father is going to live forever. But now, that milestone isn't a laughing matter because he just isn't going to make it. He's reached the end of his life journey. Tears stream down my face, standing next to my father's hospital bed while looking down upon the man who helped to give me life.

Eventually, at around 4:00 a.m., his vital statistics flatline. The monitor sounds a "code red" for Linda, who rushes in to check on my father. He is gone, and I am shattered. My oak, my strength, has been cut down. I immediately feel my blood pressure skyrocket, and my nose start to bleed.

After I collect myself, I ask Linda, who is now filling out my father's chart, "Why did you call my father Nicky? No one has ever called him by that name."

Oddly, she doesn't respond, as though she doesn't even hear me. I suddenly realize that my father had been speaking to me via Linda, letting me know that I'm going to be okay in his absence. It's incredibly reassuring, yet painful at the same time.

Four days later, my father's wake is held. To my family's astonishment, almost six hundred mourners show up to pay their respects to a man who, at some point or another, entered their lives with hope and consolation. The receiving line wraps all the way around the outside of the funeral home, taking hours—a fitting tribute to a man who did so much for so many.

People flock in from all over Florida, sharing one story after another of how my father positively impacted their life. One young woman grabs hold of my hands and tearfully shares how my father helped her get into college—a dream she'd had since early childhood. Meanwhile, a young man relays to my mother that my father co-signed on a loan so he could buy a car to attend college. He now owns his own business and is quite successful.

An older gentleman of Greek descent, quiets the entire viewing room and tells the story of how my father saved his aunt's life. According to the man, my father showed up at his family's deli one day, bearing a brown paper bag filled with money to pay for her life-saving surgery. After plopping the brown paper bag down on the counter, my father hugged the man's uncle and proceeded to make himself a roast beef sandwich.

Many others pass through the receiving line, sharing stories of how my father graciously paid their family's rent and utilities when they were immigrants, fresh off the boat from Greece. He assisted the families upwards of six months, allowing them to get on their feet financially, while also teaching them how to read and speak English as well as how to drive.

It's a tidal wave of goodwill gushing forth, with story upon story upon story being told of how my father positively impacted their lives or the lives of their loved ones. He is a legacy, a hard act to follow; he was my amazing father.

For his eulogy, I don a cap and gown and award him a college degree, while sharing tales of his inspiring life. The idea came to me in the late afternoon, a few hours before the wake was set to start. While I typed up the eulogy on my computer, Clare rushed to the local Staples to buy some parchment paper. Another one of my assistants rushed home to retrieve her son's cap and gown for me to wear.

To Nick L. Karis: an honorary degree, summa cum laude, from the University of Life, for eighty-seven years of service and devotion to family, friends, and country. That's what the parchment paper reads that I've printed out and framed. Everyone then stands and applauds him, congratulating him for earning his one and only college degree.

My father always wanted to go to college, but family circumstances prevented him. Yet, he helped so many young people get their college degrees—my brother, my sister, and me among them. Now, he can head off to Heaven without any regrets. He's earned that degree.

"Thank you for the amazing life you have given me," I say as I place the framed parchment paper inside the casket and kiss my father on the cheek, one last and final time. The pallbearers close the casket and with it, a significant chapter of my life closes as well.

Chapter Fourteen

Upon the passing of my father, my family, at one time tight-knit, loyal, and loving to each other, begins to painfully pull apart. It's as if my father, who served as the family's patriarch, was the glue that had held us all together. Now that he is gone, our family structure is falling apart at the seams.

Pent-up emotions, such as jealousy and resentment, start to surface and various factions amongst family members begin to form. Even in the strongest of families, death can cause families to split apart, or so I've been told by people who have gone through a similar situation. Although never in a million years, did I anticipate anything like this happening to my beloved family. Never. Absolutely never.

The biggest schism occurs between my sister and me. Once incredibly close, we've stopped speaking to each other. Actually, this situation arose before my father passed away but got deeper upon his passing.

The schism first occurred in early February, about ten days before my father passed away. Somehow, my sister found out that I had gone to the Bahamas months earlier with a man who was separated from his wife. Shortly before my father's passing, she called me on my cellphone one evening and slammed into me without so much as saying hello: "Did you go the Bahamas with (fictitious) Thomas?" she demanded to know.

At first, I denied it because she made it seem so wrong. But eventually, I came around and said, "Yeah, what's the big deal? It was for a business meeting, and we had separate rooms. He and his wife were separated and had already filed for divorce."

"Well, I've lost all respect for you," she said, abruptly hanging up the phone without saying another word to me.

As you might imagine, the situation made things very uncomfortable when my father was in the hospital and later at his wake because she and I weren't speaking to each other. We sort of tippy-toed around each other, ignoring each other as best we could.

Now, two months later, sitting in the tiny living room of my apartment, I am rehashing in my head that painful conversation and the ensuing split between us. Tears begin to form, recalling my sister's words: "I've lost all respect for you."

Her words cut into me like a knife that February evening on the phone, and still do, even to this day. Given our almost fourteen-year age difference, she had always been like a second mother to me. I am devastated to have lost her respect and support, all over a man who had absolutely no emotional ties to our family whatsoever.

Looking back, maybe I was wrong in going to the Bahamas with him. But he was separated from his wife, and I hadn't dated anyone since that whole nightmare experience with Mitchell, so I really thought it would be okay.

And even if it wasn't okay, isn't family supposed to stick together? My sister and I were supposed to be a bonded, powerful team, capable of taking on the world—forever. And now, well...

Suddenly, the absence of my father, the man who had always been here to support me, hits me like a ton of bricks. He was my protector, our family's protector, and I miss the strength he brought to life, including my own. If he were living, he would have made things right, by reminding all of us of the importance of sticking by family, even if we disagree with someone's actions.

I begin to sob uncontrollably, feeling incredibly vulnerable, not to mention very much alone, especially now that my oak is gone and being without a significant other to emotionally support me. My mother, the one person who I can always count on, is mourning the loss of her husband of almost sixty-two years, so I can't turn to her for consolation.

The result is that I find myself falling into a state of deep despair. What will ultimately befall me, I do not know.

Chapter Fifteen

My world now spinning out of control, I find myself angry with God again. It's far worse than the last few times I got angry with Him. Words form in my mind, harsh ones: "God, I hate you! You are a fraud!"

Feeling like no one will miss me, I even entertain fleeting thoughts about leaving this world, but I quickly push them out of my mind, knowing I could never cause harm to myself or to my mother. If I did do something drastic, my mother would be dealt a devastating second blow after recently losing my father—and I could never hurt her in that way.

This feeling of deep despair continues for another month or so when, through Divine intervention or something (I really can't say for sure what it is), I experience some sort of internal shift. I can't exactly pinpoint how or when this shift occurs, other than I know it does, but I begin to see light coming at me slowly, but surely, with awe-inspiring force.

This light appears in the form of signs and synchronicities, manifesting in my path quite frequently, sometimes several times in a given week. Their serendipitous nature helps to slowly pull me up and out of my depression and to relieve some of my grief, by providing comfort and reassurance that I will somehow survive the difficult process I am going through. One friend of mine described the process to me as being a painful, yet cathartic, dark night of the soul, and I agree. It's like I'm walking through the valley of darkness, hoping to eventually emerge fully into the light.

One evening, for example, I receive an amazing sign of serendipity related to my father, when I'm sitting at the bar of a local Italian restaurant having a bite to eat. A doctor, who once treated my father, sits down next to me and starts chatting with me about my father, saying how much he enjoyed having him as a patient. Of course, my heart is rejoicing, recounting with the doctor fond memories of my father.

Later that evening, when I'm driving home from the restaurant, I smell a man's cologne inside the Rover. I sniff my shirt, thinking that the doctor had somehow rubbed some of his cologne onto me. But my shirt doesn't smell like cologne; the smell is coming from someplace else. Where from, though, I do not know.

The smell continues to grow stronger, until I'm finally prompted to pull over to the side of the road to determine where it is coming from. I close my eyes and takes several deep breaths. Suddenly, I realize that the cologne is the same one my father used to wear.

I sit there for several minutes, taking one deep breath after another to affirm that I am, indeed, smelling his cologne. Tears well up in my eyes, and my heart feels like it's cracking wide open. At this moment, I realize my father is with me, touching me spiritually, as he only left me physically upon his death to travel to a realm beyond this one.

This realization not only comforts me, but it provides me with a sense of comfort and empowerment over the ensuing weeks and months. I still have no idea, though, who is orchestrating all of these strange, yet amazing, occurrences. Is it God? A Higher Power? Or is my father working miracles from beyond? It's a mystery I hope I am able one day to solve.

A brief time later, another amazing sign appears in my path, again related to my father. This time it happens while I'm trying a large motor vehicle accident case with Tim, my co-counsel. As he's conducting *voir dire* of potential jurors, I turn around in my chair and whisper to Clare, who is sitting behind me on one of the courtroom benches, "I wish my dad were here to see me in action."

Clare replies, "Your dad is here, and I know he's proud of you."

Next thing I know, a woman juror responds to Tim's questioning, saying that she runs her family's construction company which has contracts with the State of Florida Department of Transportation. I can't believe what I am hearing, because my father had worked as a civil engineer for the Florida D.O.T. for many, many years. But then comes the "wowser" moment which convinces me that something otherworldly is going on in the courtroom.

Tim calls on the next juror, a woman appearing to be in her mid to late seventies. Anticipating Tim's question, she rolls right into saying, "My name is Sally Abrahams. I have a high school degree. I also have an honorary degree from the University of Life, summa cum laude."

I gasp, awe-struck by this incredible serendipity. That's the same thing I wrote on the framed parchment paper that I placed in my father's casket: "an honorary degree from the University of Life, summa cum laude." It must be more than sheer coincidence because the timing of it is too impeccable for it not to be.

Wow! I'm either batshit crazy, or I'm somehow connecting into a Higher Power. I can't believe my dad is here with me. He didn't disappoint me, even after his passing, I think, trying to stay focused on jury selection while holding back the tears.

Chapter Sixteen

One week later, I'm sitting in Clare's office waiting for her to edit a document for me to sign when something intuitively prompts me to call my home answering machine, something I rarely do as I typically use my cellphone for all incoming and outgoing calls. Much to my surprise, I find myself listening to a message from Pinellas County Animal Services, informing me that Paulie is at their facility: "If you want him," the voice states firmly, "you have five days to claim him. After that, he will be at risk of being euthanized."

When I replay the message, I note the date and instantly break into a cold sweat. It's been exactly five days since the message was left, and the facility closes in half an hour.

"Clare, Clare," I say, barely able to contain myself. "Paulie is back, Paulie is back. He's at Pinellas County Animal Services. I hope to God he hasn't been put down."

"Oh, my gosh! Hurry up and call them," she replies, enthusiastically.

I frantically tap the number for PCAS into my cellphone, then hit send. A woman answers the phone and transfers me to the intake department. When a man picks up on the line, I state with desperation in my voice: "I'm calling about the hound-boxer mix, case number A45171922, that was brought in from the emergency clinic. I can be there first thing tomorrow morning, if he's still alive."

"Hold on a moment. Let me pull up his record," a man says as I anxiously wait to learn of Paulie's fate.

Finally, after what feels like an eternity (more like two minutes, in real time), the man comes back on the line and says, "Tomorrow will be fine. He's safe until then."

"Thank you so much," I say, heaving a huge sigh of relief that Paulie is still alive. I click off the call.

"What about his owner?" Clare asks.

My heart sinks to the floor for a second time. "Oh, yeah, I forgot about her," I reply, then rummage through my desk drawer for the business card she had previously given me.

Locating it, and with my hands shaking, I nervously call the number. She answers, and I relay to her that Paulie is now at Pinellas County Animal Services. I then say, "They pulled my information off the microchip he got when he was at the Humane Society. Do you want him back?"

"He's all yours," she replies. "My husband and I have given up trying to keep him contained."

I hang up the call, giddy with excitement. Paulie is back, and he's now officially, undeniably mine. He has returned to me two days shy of the six month time period I predicted he would return.

After sharing the news with Clare, she says, "That's so awesome. Now, all you need is for Mitchell to call and tell you he's transformed." She laughs and rolls her eyes.

Well, sure as day, about an hour later, as Clare and I are getting ready to leave the office, my cellphone rings. I'm in shock when I look at the caller ID—it's Mitchell, who I haven't spoken to in nearly two years.

Nervously, I answer the call. "Hey, Nik, it's Mitchell," he says. "Just calling to see how you're doing." I mouth to Clare that he's on the phone. She looks at me wide-eyed and signals goodbye, as she walks out the door.

For the next hour, he and I chat, catching up on our lives. When he tells me that he is still involved in his heated divorce and custody battle, I say, "I'm sorry to hear that. I hope your kids are doing okay."

"They are, they are," he replies. "Look, I have to go now, as I have a call coming through on the other line. I should be in your area in the next month or so and would love to get together."

"Uh, sure, that would be great," I say, not certain if I want to open the medieval door again and risk getting pulled back into Mitchell's web, as I've actually been feeling a lot more positive and optimistic without his narcissistic energy invading my thoughts.

After our call finishes, my mind runs in a million different directions, taking my emotions with it. The serendipity of Mitchell calling on the same day that I find out about Paulie is too overwhelming to deny. What it all means, and where it is all headed, though, I do not know. One thing's for certain: there's something amazing taking place in my world.

The next morning, I arrive at Pinellas County Animal Services before it opens, hoping and praying that something untoward didn't happen to Paulie overnight, as I would be devastated if it did. After what seems like an eternity, the doors finally open, and I rush inside to the front desk. I say, "I'm here for Paulie Karis. Last name starts with a *K*."

Looking at her computer screen, the receptionist says, "Row 45, kennel 137. You'll find him there. One of the kennels techs will assist you." She buzzes me through the locked door to the back of the building where the kennels are located.

As I anxiously walk through rows and rows of kennels, looking at the sad faces of the dogs behind them, my stomach is in knots, knowing that many of them will never make it out of here alive. "Something needs to be done to help these poor voiceless souls," I say, tears forming in my eyes.

And then I see him. Paulie is curled up inside his kennel, presumably clueless as to his potential fate being here. I poke my finger through the chain-link fencing and wiggle it. Looking into his sad, pitiful eyes, I say, "Hey, buddy, it looks like you've gotten yourself into another fine mess. Are you ready to come home?"

He cocks his head like he gets what I'm saying. And at once, I wave to one of the kennel techs to come assist me. The tech opens the door to the kennel, and Paulie jumps for joy as I struggle to clip the leash that I've brought with me onto his collar.

"Time to go home, buddy," I say, leading him by the leash back toward the reception area.

Once I pay his prison bill, get him out of the building, and secure him inside the Rover, I look back at him and say, "Well, buddy, it's just you and me now." I roll the back window down part way, and he immediately sticks his snout out, visibly sniffing the air. Smiling, I know he's finally back where he belongs.

Chapter Seventeen

Paulie's first month home is super challenging, as he's still a massive runner of a dog, and I am still an inexperienced dog owner. Several times a week, he manages to escape from either the house or the office. Each time that he does, I'm sent on a wild-goose chase through town, often in one of my custom-made suits and leather booties.

On a few occasions, my assistants and friends join me on the chase. Some drive after him in their car, while others pursue him on foot. No matter how we chase after him, though, it's always a hilarious visual. Fortunately, on each and every occasion, we are able to capture Paulie before he gets maimed or killed. The pursuit is usually over within fifteen minutes, although sometimes it takes upwards of an hour to save him from the calamity of the busy streets.

Thankfully, no one gets injured during these forays (although I do lose a heel on one occasion). There are, however, a lot of winded warriors who return from these adventures thankful Paulie is alive but ready to strangle him. Paulie, on the other hand, is always blissfully unaware of the distress he has caused us. He's just happy to have had a good run.

On one particular occasion, Paulie stops long enough for a kind, homeless man to feed him a hot dog before darting off down the street again. I lunge for him, but it's a split-second too late, and I end up doing a major face-plant on the sidewalk.

"This crazy mutt is trying to kill me," I say, brushing myself off before reengaging the chase.

Finally, in the beginning of June, after a particularly harrowing chase where Paulie is nearly hit by a car, I throw my hands up in futility. "I quit. This dog is more than I can handle. I can rock a courtroom, but this dog has me beat," I say, looking at Paulie in the back seat of the Rover, tongue again hanging down to the floorboard from the chase that has just ensued. Really, he must think this is a game or something.

This time, I reach for my cellphone and call Curt, a dog trainer my brother has recommended. He owns a training facility about forty-five minutes away. At this point, I'm so thoroughly exasperated that I'm willing to try anything. I need professional help—and quick. Paulie's capers are starting to interfere with my daily workload. People around town are also starting to talk about me, saying I've become "the crazy dog lady." Best to nip the trash talk in the bud, so I arrange to meet Curt the following day.

After relaying Paulie's history, he suggests that I enroll him in "doggie boot camp." Paulie will stay at the facility for several weeks, upwards of three months, for intensive training. Curt's goal will be to break Paulie of his bad and dangerous habit of running because it can only end in him getting killed. Twice a week, I will join him in a training session with the right to visit him as often as I wish.

This is the answer to my doggie prayers, I think, then sign a check for three-thousand whopping dollars and hand it to Curt. Nonetheless, I feel relieved, believing it will be money well-spent.

Four days later, on Saturday, June 8th, I drop Paulie off at boot camp and bid him a tearful goodbye. Inwardly, I feel like a huge failure, but Curt assures me that Paulie just needs a little refining. "He's been through a lot and needs to decompress. In no time, he'll be back to you," he says.

When I arrive home, I walk down the breezeway and head inside the recreation room. Over in one corner, I notice Paulie's dog bed and bowls, along with some toys and bones. I sigh, realizing how much I miss him already. The house feels so empty without him around.

Since it's Saturday, the construction workers have the day off. It's just me and my four rescue cats spread across three buildings. There are tools, buckets, brushes, plywood, and drywall scattered everywhere—evidence of construction that's been ongoing for the past four years. For the past seventeen months, since selling my other home, I've been living in the cramped quarters of the apartment above the guest house, along with my cats, and am ready for the main house to finish so I can move in.

The project is moving at a snail's pace, though. Since purchasing the home in March 2003, I've encountered one obstacle after another, from dishonest contractors to shoddy workmanship to laborers being complete no-shows. In a few particularly low moments, I've contemplated putting up a for-sale sign or worse, throwing gasoline on it and setting it on fire (just kidding, as spending time behind bars due to an arson charge is not my idea of fun). But I always stop myself, recalling the big, beautiful dream that got me to where I'm at today.

My original vision was for the house to become a place of refuge, a sanctuary for family and friends. Apparently, I first envisioned this home back in the sixth or seventh grade, when I was part of an enhanced learning program. The teacher had asked us to design our future dream home, including both the exterior and interior look.

Well, last year, when I was unpacking some boxes, I found the project tucked away with some of my old schoolwork and was shocked when I opened it. My dream home back then looked eerily similar to the home I'm now constructing from the number and type of rooms, all the way down to the cabinet detailing and colors in the kitchen. But the really crazy part is that on the final page of project I wrote: "And I want my home to be a recreation place for family and friends to enjoy." That was a wowser, all right, as I have no conscious recollection of ever having done that project.

Anyway, that dream, like so many of my other dreams, has yet to manifest, and I am growing weary as the years pass by. My heart is aching for the day when "controlled chaos" dominates my home because the quiet I repeatedly experience is difficult to bear.

"I can't wait for this nightmare to be over," I say, plopping down on the couch, wishing I could wave a magic wand and instantly finish everything that needs to be done.

Leaning back on the couch, I close my eyes and envision Paulie snoring away on his dog bed, broken of his habit of running. You know, he's had an amazing effect on me in a very short period of time. Despite the wild chases he sends me on, he's filled a huge void in my life and touched a part of my heart that I've closed off for years. It's a part of me that I keep safely hidden from the outside world, afraid that exposing it will be too painful.

If I'm really honest, I've been hurt so many times in the past that I'm afraid to fall in love. I don't want to be emotionally rejected or abandoned again, just like I was by all those bullies back in school.

To avoid this pain, I've become an expert at attracting the wrong kind of men. The vast majority of them have been huge narcissists, incapable of loving me, much less committing to me. They've been safe in terms of being non-committal, yet highly destructive to my emotional well-being. Then again, I haven't exactly been loving myself, so the men that I've been attracting have only been reflecting back my own lack of self-worth. Many of my relationships with my female friends have echoed a similar theme, as it's been one narcissistic relationship after another.

"I know I need to learn to love myself again and regain my power," I say to myself. "It's the only way to protect myself from all the narcissists in this world. I can't continue with this vicious cycle, year after year after year. It's exhausting me."

After getting up from the couch, I head upstairs to the apartment to change my clothes. Today is Saturday, and the weather is beautiful, so I've decided to take the afternoon off and spend it window shopping in nearby downtown Dunedin.

Chapter Eighteen

It's now the following day, meaning Sunday, and my mother, wanting to celebrate my father's remarkable life, has planned a small family luncheon at a local steakhouse which my father used to love. Had my father still been living, he would be celebrating his eighty-eighth birthday on this very day.

Eight close family members, including myself, show up for the affair. But it's far from a celebration, as things quickly go south, and the affair becomes the straw that finally breaks my family's proverbial back.

Without getting into the details of what precipitates it, my niece, my sister's daughter, stands up during lunch and exclaims in the crowded restaurant while pointing at me, "She's nothing but a whore. She went to the Bahamas with my friend's husband when they were separated, and now they're back together again." She storms out of the restaurant with my sister in tow.

For a moment, I'm in shock—really, really in shock, as I wasn't expecting this particular blow, at least not during a celebration like today's. Then I say, "Uh, uh, he was separated from his wife. They had already filed for divorce. And uh...it was a business trip, and we had separate rooms."

After a very long, uncomfortable pause, someone says something in my defense. Then a few others nod in agreement. The general mood among my family members is that it's my life, and I'm free to go out with and date whomever I wish.

That sentiment changes the next day, though; and quite dramatically, let me add. My family splits into four camps: one supporting my sister and niece; a second refusing to take a position; a third being my poor mother; and a fourth being me. Accusations are flying everywhere, all focused on me and the illicit lifestyle I'm supposedly living.

"Pops, where are you? I need you," I say, looking up to the heavens one evening after work, wishing he were here to help bring my family back together again. If he were still alive, none of this bullshit would be happening, absolutely none.

Thankfully, though, through all of the turmoil and grief, I have Paulie to focus on. There's a tremendous healing quality about him, and I feel calmer, stronger, and more centered with him in my life. I've never had a dog before, so I don't know if this is something all dogs provide to their owners or just rescue dogs. Whatever the case, it's like Paulie has been God-sent to help me through this incredibly difficult and challenging time.

Within a week of being at Curt's facility, I begin attending training sessions with Paulie. They are a great distraction, as they take my mind off the disintegration taking place within my family structure. Twice weekly, I learn how to walk and control Paulie on a leash while teaching him basic commands.

The sessions are difficult and tiring because my role is both that of student and teacher. I'm learning to wear a whole new hat—that of being not just a dog owner, but an owner who feels confident and in control of her dog. As challenging as it is at times, it's also exhilarating. *Sit, stay, heel, come* become a whole new vernacular for me, and I often hear these words echoing through my head as I sleep.

Paulie is strong, and he is also incredibly stubborn. My back, shoulders, and forearms often ache from the strength I must assert to control him. Yet, despite the many challenges I face, I love Paulie and can't imagine life without him in it, not for one second.

When I look into his eyes, I see a reflection of myself—flawed, imperfect, and running from all the heartaches I've endured. And I start to get it—we're both runners. God sent Paulie to me as a messenger—to show me that I'm a runner, too, and to help me figure out how to stop running.

Toward the middle of July, Curt calls. Paulie has been doing spectacular during his intensive training sessions and is ready to come home. I'm thrilled because he's been gone for two months now. In anticipation of his return, I get his bowls and bed ready for him.

When I arrive at the training facility, Paulie is on a leash, waiting in the reception area with Curt. Upon seeing me, Paulie immediately lights up. He is so elated that he plants huge slobbery kisses all over my face and wags his tail, doing several circles while jumping up and down. Instinctively, he knows that he is going home.

This time, he hops in the front passenger seat of the Rover rather than the back. As a treat, I drive to the nearest McDonald's and buy him his favorite dish: two cheeseburgers (hold the pickles, the ketchup, and the onions), which he woofs down in exactly two bites.

Afterwards, he proceeds to put his snout up to the air conditioning vent and snorts in the cold air. I laugh so hard watching him do this that I almost lose a lung. Already, he has a new antic which will put a smile on my face every time that he does it.

That night, Paulie sleeps soundly in the recreation room on his dog bed with his favorite fleece blanket and Nyla bone tucked up underneath his right shoulder. He doesn't bark or so much as make a peep. It's apparent that he's happy to be home, and I'm happy to have him back with me.

Chapter Nineteen

Energized by the fact Paulie is with me again, I rise at 5:00 a.m. the next morning. I shower then dress, grab a Diet Pepsi out of the refrigerator (a bad habit, I know), and head out the door to the office with Paulie in tow. When I arrive, it's still dark outside, but I'm not the least bit afraid because I have my canine protector by my side.

After sitting down at my desk, I take a deep breath and purvey the large stacks of court documents needing my review. During the past couple of years, things have been changing in the legal profession for personal injury attorneys like myself. In tightening their financial belts, insurance companies are requiring that almost every case worth any money be litigated through the court system, which means a boatload of additional work to bring a case to conclusion.

I sigh, thinking of all the boring legalese I will have to swallow in the coming hours. Paulie, on the other hand, has landed in clover. He rolls over and lets out a small sigh before falling back to sleep. I wish I were him, without a care in the world and someone to look after me.

At 8:30 a.m., my assistants arrive at the office and ready themselves to start the day. It's going to be a busy one, packed with phone conferences and other matters needing my attention.

Around eleven, a middle-aged client, injured in a five-car pileup a few months back, hobbles into the office to sign an affidavit. When he leaves, he fails to securely shut the front door. And you guessed it! The trigger pulled, and out the door Paulie goes on the trot. Less than twenty-four hours after completing boot camp, he is on the run again. "Motherf—" I mumble under my breath, rushing back to my office to grab my car keys.

"Hold my calls," I yell as I race out the door. "Paulie's on the run!"

"Will do," my receptionist yells back.

The Rover is parked out front of the office. So I leap inside, flip a U-turn, and swerve into the center turn lane, not wanting Paulie to get too far out of my sight. As I follow him through town, I honk at the cars in front of me to speed things along. My front windows are down, and I'm yelling at the top of my lungs, "Pauuulieeeee, get back here," while weaving back and forth between lanes.

When he makes a hard right to chase some poor cat into a yard, I up my speech and yell, "Motherfucker, get your ass in this car." He doesn't even flinch, so I slam the Rover into park, rip off my high heels, and take off after him. This is where years of playing soccer keep me from collapsing.

Eventually, I corner him in a yard three houses away, his tongue hanging down to the ground, while I'm breathing heavily. We're momentarily at a standoff. But I've had it, so I lunge forward, grab him by the collar, and practically drag him back to the car. He jumps in the back seat as if it's—yes, a game.

I'm none too happy, as you might imagine, by this so-called game Paulie apparently likes to play. Sweating profusely and looking like a wet mess, I sniff my armpits. Thankfully, my deodorant has held up.

Then before anything else, I call Curt. "Hey, Curt, this is Nikki... Well, if you can believe, Paulie ran from me again. It took me thirty minutes to catch him... Okay, I will... Yes, I'll be there within the hour... Yes, I understand."

After hanging up the call, I turn to Paulie and say, "You just bought yourself another month of boot camp. And this time, you're on your own."

This go around, Curt has requested that I visit Paulie only once a week and forego training sessions with him. He wants to work with Paulie, one on one, without outside distractions. I'm obviously worried about Paulie's welfare but have no other choice, as he's way more dog than I can handle.

I arrive at the facility forty-five minutes later—barefoot, exhausted, and exasperated. After marching inside, I hand Paulie's leash to Curt. "He's all yours," I say, then head back to the office shaken.

About a week later, I see my brother at our mother's house one afternoon. He says, "I saw Curt the other day when I dropped Bella off for boarding. Your dog is apparently keeping Curt on his toes."

"On his toes?" I ask, eyebrows raised.

"Yeah, he said something about wanting to find you another dog. He said he will keep Paulie at the facility. He can live there."

"Another dog? Why would I do that? I love Paulie," I say, feeling quite offended by the suggestion.

"Curt said he's never seen a dog like him. He said something about him being the most stubborn dog ever."

"Well, stubborn or not, Paulie is mine. He's not going anywhere, except coming home to me."

About three weeks later, Curt calls me. Paulie has finished his second round of boot camp. This time, Curt wants to personally drop Paulie off at my house. He wants to show me something.

When Curt arrives, I notice a major change in Paulie. But it's not in Paulie's demeanor; it's in his collar. Curt has configured him with a shock collar to prevent him from running away. "A shock collar? Um, I don't really like that idea. He might get injured by it," I say.

"It's just a harmless shock, something to momentarily stun him, so you can grab hold of him. All you have to do is hit this button when he starts to run," Curt says, referencing the remote clicker in his hand. "Believe you me, he will stop dead in his tracks."

Well, so much for the *believe you me* part. Not thirty seconds later, while the three of us are underneath the massive oak tree in my back yard, something triggers Paulie. Suddenly, he takes off like a bat of out hell, heading down the hill toward the bayou. Curt immediately hits the clicker, but Paulie is already out of striking distance.

"Damn it! This dog is impossible," he says before taking off after him, futilely jabbing the clicker.

I chuckle, watching Curt chase after Paulie, then run inside, grab my car keys, and hop into the Rover. While Curt pursues Paulie on foot, I pursue him from behind the wheel. Having the edge, I catch Paulie about half a mile away. He hops into the back seat, now leashed but unfazed. A few seconds later, I pull up beside Curt, who is visibly winded, walking back toward my house.

"Would you like a ride?" I ask him.

"Nah, I'm fine. I prefer to walk," he says.

After pulling into the driveway, I let Paulie into the recreation room where he promptly laps up a full bowl of water. Meanwhile, Curt returns and is standing by his car, ready to leave. I grab Paulie by the leash and bring him back outside.

"Are you going somewhere?" I ask Curt.

Curt hands me the clicker and says, "You know, over the past three decades, I've trained thousands of dogs of all different kinds—from big to small, fluffy to short-haired, service dogs, military dogs, you name it—and I've been successful with 99.9% of them. You happen to have that one dog in a million that simply cannot be trained."

Without another word, Curt gets into his car and drives away.

Chapter Twenty

Curt now gone, I stand in the driveway stunned, not knowing quite what to do. I try calling him on his cellphone, but he doesn't answer. Now, I'm pissed because he guaranteed a 100% successful outcome in training Paulie. How dare he just drive away.

"There's three-thousand dollars down the drain," I say, looking down at Paulie, who is leaning his broad, muscular body into my legs. He keeps pushing his body harder and harder into me.

Suddenly, I realize what he's trying to say to me, so I reach down and remove the shock collar. Then I take him by the leash into the side yard, where we both sit in the grass. And for the first time ever, he sits next to me as close as he can, like he's snuggling up to me. Instantly, my heart becomes filled by the tenderness of the moment.

Reflecting, I realize Paulie and I are similar creatures. We've both been hurt, painfully hurt. He runs. I run. He runs again. I run again.

And while I don't exactly run physically, I do continue to attract emotionally unavailable men. It's running, just of a different kind. Running has become familiar to me, the same way running has become familiar to Paulie. Hopefully, with time, both of us will heal from the pains of our past and stop running, forever.

I really wish I knew his full story—when and how it all began for him. One thing's for certain: he's endured something painful, some kind of neglect or abuse which is mollified by running because he's always looking for that window of opportunity when he can escape.

Stroking him up and down his body, I say, "Look, buddy, I know you've been through some tough times. Me, too; I get it. We're going to get through this together. It's time for a fresh start for both of us. Let's try some love and affirmation, okay?"

And as unbelievable as it may sound, from that day forward, things begin to get better with Paulie—not perfect, but better. Pure, unconditional love with some boundary-setting starts to work miracles.

Over time, Paulie settles into a happier, more balanced routine. He starts coming into the office with me every day where his activities include lying on his dog bed, while I dote on him in between working and talking with clients. We also take several short walks together, so he can go potty and sniff all the interesting smells along the way.

Often, he ventures down the hallway and visits with my assistants, before making his way back to my office. If I need to run errands, I usually take him with me, windows of the Rover down, his snout in the breeze, eyes shut, soaking up the sun. Whenever I run inside somewhere, I park the car where I can see it and leave the engine running, air conditioning blasting, not wanting Paulie to overheat.

Paulie loves the Rover—really loves it—so much so that when we get home, he often refuses to go into the recreation room. Instead, he plants himself firmly in the portico, refusing to budge his massive seventy-five pound body, wanting to go back inside the Rover. Maybe the Rover has become a safe haven for him, a secure place of refuge, or maybe it's the cold air—or both.

When I try cajoling him, he turns his head the other way as though in an act of defiance. Eventually, though, he softens, releasing his resistance. Together, we head inside the recreation room where he laps us some water before flopping down on his dog bed. I'm beginning to think he does this for the extra attention as part of another game. You know, a rescue dog's way of demanding attention before showing their affection.

In the fall, I decide to take a week-long trip to Ecuador and the Galapagos Islands with my mother. She and I need some time away together, and this particular trip has been on my bucket list for quite a while. I hire Jake, who does construction at my home, to care for Paulie since the two have really bonded.

The plan is for Paulie to stay in the sixty-by-eight-foot dog run located behind the recreation room. There's an airconditioned room at one end of the run with a dog door that Paulie can go in and out of, freely. I figure he will enjoy being at home much more than being cooped up in a kennel at the vet's office.

On our way back home, and while my mom and I are waiting to clear customs in Miami to catch our flight to Tampa, I call Clare. "Mom and I are in Miami," I say to Clare after she answers the phone. "Just calling to see how things are going. How's Paulie's? Have you heard from Jake?"

"I spoke with Jake yesterday afternoon. He said Paulie is doing great. It's like he isn't even there."

"Aww, that's so awesome. I can't wait to see my boy. Can you pick us up at the airport? We land at 3:00 p.m. on American Airlines."

"Sure thing. See you curbside."

After deboarding at Tampa International Airport, my mom and I head to the baggage terminal, grab our bags from the carousel, and head outside to look for Clare. Five minutes later, she pulls up curbside in the Rover. I throw our bags into the back hatch, then open the back passenger door for my mom. Once she is safely inside, I hop into the front passenger seat.

"Good to see you, Clare. I'm glad to be home," I say, closing the door.

"Great to see you both as well," she says.

"I can't wait to see Paulie. Can you—?" I don't even finish my sentence when Clare interrupts me.

"Um, there's something I need to tell you."

"Oh my gosh! Is Paulie all right?"

"Yeah, yeah, he's fine. He just got himself into a little trouble while you were away; that's all."

Clare then relays the details of Paulie's latest adventure. It started two days ago when Jake went to feed him and discovered he had escaped from the dog run. He had called Clare in a panic.

"I was on a call with a client when Jake called," she says. "When he told me Paulie had escaped from the run but that the gate was still locked, I asked him, 'What in the hell did he do? Fucking grow wings and fly?'"

I laugh. "Well, that's my boy. He likes to keep us on their toes."

"Toes, my ass. I was ready to kill him."

According to Clare, Jake finally figured out that Paulie had scaled a mound of pavers stored on the run, jumped the wrought-iron fence, and landed on a large white bird of paradise on the other side (Jake actually found Paulie's collar hanging on one of the stalks). Once Clare got word of the escape, she sent out squads of people looking for him. They posted "lost dog" flyers all around town.

Thankfully, a few hours later, a man saw one of the flyers at the local convenient store. He called Clare to let her know that he and his wife had found Paulie and taken him to the Humane Society.

"Well, the Humane Society it is. I'm sure they will be totally thrilled to see me again," I say, letting out a chuckle. "Let's get there before it closes. I want to break my boy out of jail."

When we arrive at the Humane Society, I fill out some paperwork verifying that Paulie is, indeed, mine. I mean, seriously, who else would want to claim this wayward pooch anyway? He's cost me a fortune in training and mental anguish, not to mention pushing me to the limits of my physical capabilities.

But we are super connected, he and I, destined to be together. So I fork over some cash to the woman at the front desk to compensate the Humane Society for its trouble. I then load him into the back of my Rover but when

I do, he turns his head the other way, completely ignoring me. *He's so predictable*, I think, chuckling at his antics.

Clearly, he's snubbing me again. Maybe, he's mad I ruined his little runaway party or that I took a trip without him. Or maybe, just maybe, he sees all of this as being one big game, like the caterpillar that climbs and climbs and climbs the pillar, having no idea what is actually at the top.

Chapter Twenty-One

Forty-five minutes later, after dropping Clare off at the office and then my mom at her house, Paulie and I arrive home. He immediately retreats into the recreation room where, without drinking any water or eating any food, he flops down on his dog bed and falls fast asleep. His adventures the past couple of days have apparently worn him completely out.

The next day, we return to our happy routine, spending our days at the office and early evenings hanging out in the side yard waiting for the sun to set. I've now reduced my work schedule to twelve hours a day, starting at 6:00 a.m. and finishing at 6:00 p.m., in order to spend some quality time with Paulie at home. It's a refreshing change to my everyday routine.

During our evening outings, Paulie looks so peaceful and content, like he's finally accepted my love. It's like he was testing me before, but now he knows where he belongs, with me at home where he's safe from the perils of the outside world. My love is transforming him; and in return, he is transforming me. Slowly, but surely, I feel my heart starting to heal and opening up to love again with the once-runner Paulie showing me the way.

You know, dogs are so amazing. Since the day I rescued Paulie from that parking lot, he has taught me so many valuable life lessons while showering me with unconditional love. All the trouble he has put me through during the past year and a half, while distressing at the time, has been more than worthwhile because he has blessed me beyond measure.

Then one afternoon, as our happy routine approaches the end of six months, I notice a cyst on Paulie's right shoulder. Concerned, I take him to the vet, who suggests a biopsy to rule out the Big C. The biopsy is scheduled for two days later.

On the morning of the biopsy, I drop Paulie off at the vet before heading to my office. Shortly after noon, I'm hungry and decide to go to the grocery store to get something to eat, absentmindedly leaving my cellphone at the office. While I'm in the store, I suddenly feel sick and start dry-heaving, like I did that night in the parking lot when my father was admitted to the emergency room. I'm nauseous to the point I can't see straight, and I leave the store in a daze, without getting what I've gone there to buy.

When I arrive back at the office, I sit down at my desk and look at my cellphone, noticing that I've missed two calls from the vet's office. Instantly, I know that something is terribly wrong. In a panic, and hoping I'm overreacting, I call the vet's office and get body-slammed. During his biopsy, Paulie went into atrial fibrillation, and the vet made the decision to let him go. I'm completely gutted.

"What do you mean he's gone?" I ask the vet. "What do you mean!"

Without giving the vet time to respond, I slam down the phone on my desk and storm out of my office, driving straight to the vet clinic which is located less than ten minutes away. The receptionist immediately escorts me back to see him.

"I want a fucking answer," I yell to the vet, my teeth clenched and fists pounding on his desk, while tears stream down my face. "You killed Paulie, and I want him back. I just want him back."

Sobbing uncontrollably, I drop down into the chair behind me. The vet starts crying, too. He says, "Nikki, I'm sorry. I'm so, so sorry. I tried to save him, but he kept going into atrial fib. I had to let him go. It was the hardest thing I've done in a long time, as I haven't lost a dog on the table in years."

I don't respond because the tears won't stop flowing. And the pain, well, I've never felt anything this intense before, not even when my father passed away. It's like a part of me died with Paulie on the operating table.

The vet then pulls out some X-rays and shows them to me. "Here, Nikki. Take a look at these," he says, mounting them on a lighted board.

I reach for some tissues on his desk, wipe away the tears, and blow my nose. My efforts to focus on the x-rays are futile, however, because the tears are stinging my eyes.

"Please, come closer," the vet says. I rise from my chair and move toward the lighted board. "I took these X-rays of his heart because I wanted you to see. His heart was very enlarged, one of the largest I've ever seen. It was likely caused from all the running he did."

"Running?" I ask.

"Yeah, I think all that running did him in."

I sit back down in the chair and start bawling once again. Running—that's what killed Paulie; his fear of being loved killed him in the end. No matter how much I loved him, it wasn't enough to heal his heart from the pains of his past.

As though reading my mind, the vet says, "You gave him the best life possible. No one else would have loved him as much as you did, no one. In the end, he knew you loved him."

I finally calm down enough to respond coherently. "Thanks, Doc. And my apologies; I got carried away. It wasn't your fault."

The vet hugs me. "It's okay, Nikki. Losing a pet is one of the worst things that can happen to us. They become a huge part of our life."

"No question, they do. I never knew such love existed, until I rescued Paulie."

I leave his office and stop at the front desk to pay my bill. "Doc said there's no charge for today," the receptionist says. "We're all so sorry for your loss. But we do need you to pick an urn, if you wish to have him cremated."

"Yes, of course," I respond as I look over the photos of the urns the receptionist has provided me. I pick out a beautiful brass urn etched with dog paws with a matching nameplate that reads, "Paulie Knuckles No Fears Karis," then exit the clinic.

Once inside my car, I sit in silence, sobbing for what feels like an eternity. It's like my heart is tearing in two. Paulie, my wayward mutt, the dog who caused me so much grief yet brought me so much love, is gone— forever. The heartache is almost unbearable.

I wipe my face on the sleeve of my shirt and head for home. As I do, I think back to November 19, 2006, the day when I saw Paulie lying in that parking lot, and the man rode up on the bicycle wearing the *Hope for the Flowers* t-shirt. Reflecting on it all, I get the distinct feeling that something much bigger is about to occur in my life. What that is exactly, I do not know.

Chapter Twenty-Two

Three days have passed, since Paulie unexpectedly left the Earthly plane and traveled onto the Rainbow Bridge. And while I'm trying to move forward, my grief is overwhelming at times, as I find myself crying at the mere thought of him. His scent lingers everywhere—on my clothes, in the recreation room, in the Rover, at the office, and every other place he and I ever ventured together. When it enters my nose, I'm triggered with fond memories of our final months together—then comes the flood of tears.

I half expect Paulie to burst out of his doghouse at any moment, trotting down the dog run, tongue wagging gleefully, and looking back at me in only the way he could—with that knuckleheaded glint in his eye. But he's now gone—forever—although he will never be forgotten. He changed my life, or rather *changed me*, in ways I could have never imagined.

Paulie Knuckles No Fears Karis—his proper name—had no record of his birth. I had no idea when he was born or how old he was, although the vet estimated five or six years at the time of death. How he came into this world, or where, I had no idea either.

One thing's for sure—he didn't come out of his mother's womb waving official papers, as he wasn't a purebred, pedigree, or anything even remotely close. It's even highly doubtful that his mother and father were selected to mate and procreate based upon his ancestral lineage. He was just a Heinz 57 mutt—a whole lot of somethings all mixed together—but an incredibly handsome dog with lots of charm and charisma, who made his presence known in a very big way.

From the moment I rescued him that fateful November day, he earned his official title. They were words evocating my deep fondness for him: Paulie, after Trina Paulus, the author of *Hope for the Flowers*; Knuckles, for knucklehead, on account of his stubbornness; No Fears, because he would run between the cars with no fear of the harm that might befall him; and Karis, of course, because of his unbreakable bond with me.

I miss that knucklehead so much. There is this humongous void weighing on my heart that just won't go away.

Looking back, I realize that during the year Paulie was with me, so much transpired in my life. It's like God had decided to start cleaning my relationship house, personally and, in some instances, professionally, and He sent Paulie to be my Goddog and canine protector during that process—to provide me with much needed comfort and support.

Many a time, God threw back the veil and showed me the truth; or rather, prodded me to see the truth of just how unhealthy certain relationships were in my life. He forced me to see relationship patterns and to begin making some necessary, but long overdue, changes. Mind you, I'm only in the initial phase of this massive *clean-up my relationships* project, but I'm already feeling lighter and more optimistic with every step taken.

Like Paulie had clung to running, I had clung to toxic relationships because it's all I knew, part of growing up inside a box. Every facet of my upbringing from cultural norms to the tenets of my religion to family members who served as my role models, shaped and molded this box and, in turn, me into becoming a people pleaser who never rocked the boat. My lack of self-esteem only amplified these unhealthy relationship patterns, creating a vicious cycle that was difficult to escape.

The result—I took it on the chin in many of my relationships. I repeatedly put my wants and needs second to the other person and rarely spoke my true feelings. And yes, I had been afraid to let go of toxic relationships for fear of ending up alone.

But with Paulie, I never felt alone because he was always there for me as a guiding and supporting spirit. I felt empowered to take on the harshness of the world, to begin to stand up for myself, and to start setting healthy boundaries in my relationships, even if it meant losing the other person.

I'm not sure if Paulie was channeling a Higher Power to me; or if he was that Higher Power. I don't really know for sure. Either way, I like to think that if God were to exist in the physical realm, He would be a Goddog like Paulie was to me. Maybe it's no coincidence that God spelled backward is *dog*, and when put together they spell *Goddog*.

And then there's Mitchell. With Paulie now gone, I realize any hope of Mitchell transforming and becoming my long-awaited Stripe must die as well. But that's fine, isn't it?

Thinking about the past, I realize that Mitchell came into my life when my self-esteem was at an all-time low. I was desperate to find someone to fill a void existing inside of me; and instead of looking inward for completion, I looked outward for someone to make me whole. As a result, I clung to fantasies of a narcissist and a relationship that would never come to be, hoping to be saved.

God hadn't delivered an asshole to my doorstep as I once thought; rather, He had delivered a valuable life lesson about learning to love and value myself. Had I done so, I would have never allowed Mitchell to take advantage of me like I did.

Now, I need to own it and learn my life lessons from it. Sure, I've had some shitty blows to my self-esteem through the years—stuff I didn't ask for, nor deserve, but I can't continue acting or feeling like a victim for the rest of my life. It's time to face the music, so to speak.

I'm still perplexed, though, by the man who appeared on the bicycle the day that I rescued Paulie. Then there's the magazine article about Mitchell's kids that I fell upon at the emergency vet. And what about

Mitchell calling me the very same day I played that message from Pinellas County Animal Services?

What do all of these mysterious happenings mean? They can't all be coincidences, can they? Or are they all intertwined for a greater purpose? I struggle to connect the spiritual dots, to find meaning in all that has happened. One day soon, I hope it will all become clear. Right now, though, it's all still so confusing.

Looking at the time, it's 7:00 a.m., and I realize that I'm late leaving for the office. I don't want to go to work today, but there is a huge pile of documents on my desk needing my attention. *What I wouldn't give to just skip town,* I think, but I've got responsibilities—huge ones. Paying bills, finishing this house, running my law practice, taking care of my clients— all of these things consume me, leaving little time to pursue my dreams, whatever they may be.

I give my cat, Barney, a belly rub before I head out the door. In 1994, when I moved out of my parents' house into an apartment, I adopted him from the same Humane Society to which Paulie made his way on two separate occasions.

The day I went to the Humane Society, a young girl was in the cat kennels with her grandmother petting a beautiful, steel gray kitten. I had my eye on two black kittens and was just about to exit the kennel to adopt them when she handed me the gray kitten. She said, "Pick him." The little girl was absolutely precious, blonde hair, blue eyes, and chubby cheeks which had the biggest dimples. How could I say "no" to her?

Adopting the gray kitten ended up being one of the best decisions I've ever made. I named him Barney, meaning "son of comfort," a most appropriate name that popped into my head when I was driving home with him that day.

Barney has the most amazing spirit about him. Whenever I am experiencing difficult times, he will crawl on top of me and snuggle in as close as he can get. Sometimes, he will lay across my neck, all seventeen pounds of him. It's like he can read my mind and feel my emotions because he knows exactly when I need comforting most. Remarkably, he has also managed to convert several former non-cat people into cat lovers including Clare, who didn't care for cats before meeting him.

My relationship with Barney, though, is different than the relationship I had with Paulie. Barney is like an angel, a cat with wings, who connects with me telepathically. Paulie, on the other hand, was far more primal in nature. Whenever I touched him, it felt like a part of God was shot directly into my veins; or least, I think that's what it was because I've actually never seen God in the physical realm—well, not until I rescued Paulie, that is.

"I love you, big guy. I'll see you later on today," I say to Barney, rubbing his belly for a second time.

Before heading out the door, I rub the heads of my other three cats, Koukla, Kenya, and Montana. They are all so sweet and special to me. Each one has a unique story of how they came into my life. Those stories, though, will have to wait for another day because I'm late getting to my office.

Chapter Twenty-Three

As is my daily habit, when I arrive at my office, I begin perusing the stacks of documents piled on top of my desk. Amidst the mountain of paperwork is a twenty-five page motion prepared by none other than William Wright III, as Mrs. Desuth's case is still ongoing. *This guy is relentless. He never lets up!* I think, leaning forward in my chair and scanning the motion.

The lawsuit has been moving at a snail's pace due to Billy Boy and his squad of zombies continually filing one motion after another. This motion will take Clare the better part of two days to research and respond to and another half-day for me to review and edit.

I sigh, longing for the day when I can express myself creatively and not have to keep my thoughts confined to a highly-constricted box, as there is only so much creativity you can instill into a legal document in between all the requisite wherefores, therefores, and heretofores. I put the motion into Clare's inbox with a sticky note: *Please prepare prompt response. See Juanita Smith's case for basic format.*

Growing tired of reviewing documents, I power on my desktop computer and start searching the Internet for a dog to adopt, in hopes of filling the giant hole left by Paulie in some small way. I've decided that's what I need to heal my broken heart, a canine companion to help me traverse this next stage of my journey.

A Google search brings up a number of hits, all linking back to various adoption sites. I choose PetFinder.com, since I've heard about it somewhere along the way. After inputting some limited criteria, such as the fact I'm looking for a dog and live in the Tampa Bay area, up pops a panel of dog photos.

What will appeal to me is anyone's guess, although there are certain requirements which I've drawn for myself. I'd rather not have a massive beast, meaning nothing over a hundred pounds. By contrast, a small dog like a chihuahua won't do either because their yappy bark makes me cringe. All I know is that when the right dog appears on the screen, I will know it, regardless of any preconceptions.

Clare walks into my office. "Hey, whatcha up to?" she asks.

"Trying to find my next dog. My heart needs healing. By the way, there's a motion from Billy Boy in your box that needs responding to ASAP," I say as I scroll through the photos.

"Well, if I didn't know better, I would think that Billy Boy has a huge crush on you. I think he files those motions just so he can see you in court," Clare says with a giggle.

"Yeah, right! I'm hardly his type; nor he, mine."

Clare, who has been looking over my shoulder while I scroll through puppy options, slaps my shoulder and says, "Go back."

I look back at her inquisitively, and she adds, "To the puppy you were just at. There's something about that one."

After tapping the back arrow, I stop at a cute six-month old hound puppy, brown in color, looking quite pathetic in his photo. "That's the one," say she says. "Pick him."

Leaning into the computer screen, I swear for the life of me that the puppy's hound-like eyes speak to me: *I love you, Nikki. Please pick me, please, please, please.* In this moment, his puppy eyes touch my heart, but I'm not as sure as Clare. The day before when I was out shopping, I'd seen two greyhounds up for adoption and had fallen in love with them.

Clare persists, so I send a message requesting information on the puppy. "There. It's sent," I say to her. "Now, I just have to wait."

A couple of hours later, I receive a call on my cellphone from a woman who is involved with the puppy's adoption process. "Yes, he's still available," she says. "He's at a high-kill shelter located in Lithia. According to the shelter manager, he's quite a handful."

"Quite a handful" after Paulie needs explaining, so I question her about the puppy's demeanor because I want to learn as much as I can.

"Um, I don't know exactly," she says when I pointedly question her.

"Look, if you're interested," she finally says, "you need to let me know right away. He's set to be euthanized in an hour."

"Euthanized? Oh gosh, no, I can't let that happen. I'll take him," I say, going purely by instinct and believing that I came upon his photo for a reason, or rather Clare did. Besides, how much of handful can a six-month-old puppy be?

"Great. I'll call the shelter and let them know to pull him. I'll pick him up tomorrow around noon. You can come to my house at six, okay?" she asks.

"Sure, that's fine," I reply, after taking a quick look at my calendar. "Do I need to fill out any paperwork? Pay an adoption fee? Anything like that to make this official?"

"Normally, we request both from an adopter. But in this instance, we are waiving all that. We just want to get him out of the shelter before he dies. I'll email you my address shortly."

"Okay, well, thank you so much. I will see you tomorrow then," I say, hanging up the call.

For the next few minutes, I sit at my desk, staring at the puppy's photo on my computer screen, feeling a huge amount of excitement and anticipation. Tomorrow, I'm adopting this precious little boy—my second dog ever. I can't wait to see what the future holds for us.

Chapter Twenty-Four

At 5:30 p.m. the following evening, I leave my office and head straight to the house of the woman who pulled the puppy from the shelter. When I arrive, she is outside with an older dog who is on a leash.

"Hey, I'm Beverly," she says when I exit the Rover. "You must be Nikki."

"Yes, I am. Nice to meet you."

"You as well. Let me run into the house and get the puppy for you. Can you hold this guy for a moment?"

"Uh, yeah, sure thing," I reply, taking the leash from her as she heads inside the house.

After a long, few minutes, she returns with the puppy. "Here he is. Isn't he a cutie?" she says, handing me the wriggling puppy while I still have the leash in my hand.

"He's larger than I imagined him to be," I say.

Then again, he's around six months old, so he's not exactly an infant—more like a toddler actually with a head that he's still not grown into. He weighs about thirty-five pounds by the feel of things, and it takes all my strength to keep him from escaping my hands. "But he's adorable, that's for sure. Um, hold on a moment... Let me give you this leash." I then awkwardly hand her the leash with one hand while trying to keep hold of the wriggling puppy with the other.

Suddenly, I get a whiff of a stench emitting from the ball of fur that I'm holding. "Holy cow! He stinks to high heavens," I exclaim, recalling the wretched stench emanating from Paulie the day I rescued him.

"It's shelter stench. All rescues dogs who come from shelters smell the same way. A couple of washes, and he will be good to go."

"Um, okay," I respond, trying to hold him at a distance, hoping to avoid getting bathed with his stench.

"Look, I have to walk this dog before his adopter gets here. Thanks a million for adopting this boy," she says.

"You're welcome, and thanks for getting him to me."

She takes off down the street with the dog on the leash in tow. Honestly, I'm a bit confused. I expected the adoption process to be more formal, but I'm not going to argue. The puppy is now mine.

Standing at the back of the Rover, I try to maneuver open the back hatch with the nameless puppy squirming like mad. "Hold still little fella," I say to him exasperated as he fights me with all his might, his stench now lathered all over me.

He pees on me, and I cringe, grossed out by the warm stream of urine now running down my leg. "I hope I haven't made a mistake with you!" I exclaim, thinking that I very well may have.

Finally, I get the back hatch open. I load the puppy into the Rover and put him inside a wire crate that I've borrowed from a neighbor. Needing a paper towel to wipe the urine off my jeans, I look around for some, but there are none to be found—karma, I suppose, in retaliation for my OCD; or it may just be plain bad luck.

I jump into the driver's seat, jeans wet and smelling like dog pee. Gone are the days when I wouldn't be caught dead looking or smelling like anything less than a perfectly coiffed Barbie doll. Dog fur and dog stench are now a part of my attire, although I must admit that I do wear them well.

Despite the balmy Florida heat outside, I ride with the windows down. Once or twice, I gag when I stop at a light and get a whiff of the stench emanating from the back. The smell of dog urine stays with me throughout the ride, making the ride home a miserable one.

Thirty minutes later, I pull into the portico, grab the puppy, and take him inside the recreation room. I place him inside the large basin sink and begin lathering him up with some of Paulie's leftover dog shampoo. He fights me the whole time but not as bad as before. The stench does wash off but in the process of soaping him, I notice something disheartening. His tail is crooked, like it has been broken before. *I sure hope this isn't a sign of abuse*, I think, not able to imagine anyone harming an innocent creature like him.

The puppy finally calms down; and my nerves do as well. I wash him a second time and wrap him in a warm towel. To make sure he's okay, I sit with him on the couch and gently stroke him so he knows his life is going to change for the better. Soon he falls asleep.

Noticing some remnants of Paulie's dog food on the floor, I place the puppy down on the couch and grab the dust buster. I certainly don't want the puppy eating any of it because it might upset his tummy. When I turn the dust buster on, however, the puppy suddenly wakes up and charges at it, biting at it in a jabbing-like fashion.

"Stop! Stop! Please stop," I plead with him until his fury ceases. Then I pick him up and cradle him like a baby, thinking he must have been abused in some fashion associated with a loud noise.

"Oh, my goodness, you, poor sweet soul," I say, gently rubbing his belly. He licks my face several times, obviously having been traumatized somewhere along the way. "I promise you, little buddy. No one, absolutely no one, is going to hurt you ever again," I continue, then put him back down on the couch and wrap him inside a blanket, hoping to make him feel safe and secure. He falls asleep again, finally giving me a chance to shower and change my clothes.

Over the next three days, the puppy begins to settle into his new life. Because I'm still living in the upstairs apartment, I make him a nice, comfortable bed inside the recreation room. What I learn is that it's not just dust busters that scare him. Most small appliances, even electronic drills, totally unnerve him; and he shies away from me whenever I make any quick movements. Although I'm no dog expert at this stage in my life, these tendencies suggest that he was abused in the past. His behavior eerily parallels the way abused people act, and I've seen a ton of them in my law practice. I recognize abuse when I see it.

Recognizing that the puppy needs some help, I promptly hire a trainer to work with him. But before he undergoes training, he needs a name. I blow through a list of names like Rudy, Van Gogh, and Tucker. Usually things like names easily present themselves to me but not this time, as none of them ring true his puppy's personality. He's a funny little guy with a bit of a mischievous streak, but who is also incredibly loving.

Two days later, I come home from work in the afternoon to check on the puppy. My house is still under major construction and Jake, who really loves the puppy, is still working for me. He loves the puppy so much that he's offered to look after him while I'm at work. This is a huge blessing because the puppy is in the midst of potty training and too rambunctious to take to the office.

When I enter the master bedroom, a light bulb (in my head) suddenly flicks on. The puppy, excited to see me, runs through a large pile of sawdust, getting it all over his paws. He then jumps up on me and lands a perfect set of pawprints on the black pants that I'm wearing. Without thinking, I blurt out, "Picasso!" And the name sticks, just like that, ushering in a whole new phase of my life in which my creative juices begin to flow.

Chapter Twenty-Five

From the day I choose Picasso's name, creative ideas begin to move through me like a raging river. It's like a massive dam that had been blocking the artistic side of my brain since early childhood has been felled in one swoop. Of course, I don't know if my connection with Picasso is causing this. All I know is that I'm back to creating, and this is bringing me extreme joy.

My witching hours are usually between two and four in the morning when my creativity is at its peak. It's like God channels through me at this time because ideas strike out of nowhere as I sleep.

Once an idea pops into my head, I'm immediately prompted to wake. Blurry-eyed, I search for the pen and journal I've stuffed under the bed covers for moments like this. Using the light of my cellphone, I quickly jot the idea down before it disappears from my consciousness. I then fall back to sleep for a couple of hours before rising to start the day.

Back in high school, I did a similar thing. Starting my freshman year, I joined the school newspaper, working my way up from a sportswriter to editor-in-chief by my senior year. I rarely slept back then. Instead, I spent those precious, early-morning hours writing or bent over a lightboard at the kitchen table, manually laying out the next edition of the paper. That's before high-tech computers took over and made the job a thousand times easier.

Being a journalist was my dream job back. I had a talent for writing, connecting with people, and telling their stories. One summer, at a journalism camp held at the University of South Carolina, I walked away with five awards, something never achieved before by anyone attending the camp.

As I walked up to the podium to accept the fifth and final award, I thought, *This is what I want to do with my life. I can combine my writing skills with my verbal communication skills and really affect people's lives.*

But when I told my father that I wanted to major in journalism, he was less than supportive. "You'll never make any money at it. Major in political science, then go to law school," he said, his eyes looking up at me over the top of his newspaper.

So that's what I did. I followed his sage advice—I majored in political science and applied to law school—as he was my father and never had anything but the best of intentions when it came to me. Besides, I thought that's what a child was supposed to do—follow their parent's advice, short of following that parent off a cliff.

How my college and law school years actually fared—well, that's a long story for another day. Mind you, my grades were exceptional, and I managed to graduate on time. I just had a very hard time finding where I belonged, but I guess that's to be expected after coming off the emotional trauma I suffered during high school.

Now, though, I realize that I followed my father's idea of who I should become versus pursuing my own path. I'm not mad at him, not at all. He suggested what he thought was best for me, and I followed that advice without question. But now that my oak is gone, I'm free to pursue the path calling to my soul. I can finally climb out of the box I've allowed others to construct for me and become the person I am meant to be.

It's now mid-June 2008, and I search for the folder that I've tucked away in a drawer since 2001. The folder is like the Holy Grail to me as it contains notes for a clothing line, a children's series called "Sammy Says," and other inspiring ideas, but most importantly for *The Toad Chronicles*, the book

I've envisioned writing. This time around, though, I see *The Toad Chronicles* as an entire series, helping women like myself who have yet to find their Prince Charming.

"Yes, this is it! This series is going to lead us to the Promised Land," I exclaim as Picasso cocks his head to the side, letting me know that he understands what I'm saying.

Gosh, I love him. I'm so grateful Clare pushed me to send that email about adopting him. "Thank you for the inspiration, sweet boy. Enough of the everyday grind of practicing law." I rub his head, kiss his face all over, and power on my laptop.

Although it's been seven years, I dive in and begin putting my ideas for the series into writing as if no time had passed. For the next two months, Picasso and I work side by side, formulating the ideas for the series, naming the toads, and putting together an outline of the chapters for book one. I'm in my happy place, as it feels good to break away from the boring drain of drafting legal documents.

While I type away on my laptop, Picasso lies next to me on the couch with his head on my stomach and paws propped on my thighs. It's like he is channeling to me through my sacral chakra, an energy center in the body through which creativity flows. Perhaps, he's channeling the greatness of Picasso himself because my creative juices are flowing non-stop.

"All of this is brilliant, little man. I don't know exactly what you've done to me but whatever it is, keep doing it," I say to Picasso, who rolls over for a belly rub. I scratch his belly several times, before returning to my laptop.

During this time, undeniable signs and synchronicities continue to occur in my life, confirming that I'm on the right path with my ideas. One night, for example, I'm at a friend's house hanging out when her daughter (who is in middle school) starts nervously talking nonstop about something. Sensing her anxiety, I suggest that she try finding Zen by meditating to calm herself. I then demonstrate to her how to sit cross-legged in a lotus position with her eyes closed and mouth shut while taking deep breaths through her nose. The young girl meditates for about two seconds, before she returns to her jabbering. Something then prompts me to blurt out, "Zip it, Zeni!"

I have no idea where the name Zeni comes from because I've never heard it before, but it suddenly it occurs to me that Zeni should be the name of the protagonist of *The Toad Chronicles* series. It also strikes me that I should form an inspirational company called Finding Zeni, and Zeni should serve as its spokesperson. The company will be dedicated to empowering people to become the authentic person God intended them to be, not the person others want, need, or expect them to be—the very issue I am currently struggling with in my own life.

When I get home later evening, I do a Google search for the meaning of the name Zeni. Lo and behold, the name means "God's grace," the exact concept I wish to portray via *Finding Zeni.* I'm flabbergasted, as I could not have picked a more perfect name for my new company.

Feeling more inspired than ever, I look up towards the heavens and say, "Thank you, God, Dad, or whoever is channeling all of these amazing ideas to me because there is absolutely no way I could ever conjure up this stuff on my own."

And then feeling my creative juices starting to flow as a result of this incredible serendipity which has just occurred, I begin jotting down ideas that I hope will change my life— forever.

Chapter Twenty-Six

Remarkably, two weeks later, I receive even stronger confirmation that my creative ideas are ones that I should pursue. I'm new to this channeling stuff (or whatever it is that's been going on with me), so it's comforting to know my instincts are guiding me correctly.

It happens one evening when I'm having dinner with Theo, a friend from high school. His father, when he was living, was good friends with my father. They are literally buried a stone's throw from each other in the local cemetery.

Theo asks me how my series is coming along, as word of its creation has apparently spread around town. "Great, great, the ideas are totally coming together," I reply, then tell him the amazing story of how I chose Zeni as the name for the protagonist.

"I've never heard that name before," he says.

"I hadn't either. Ever since my dad died, and then my dog Paulie, and now with Picasso in my life, I've been getting all sorts of signs and synchronicities. I don't know if my father has been channeling them, or if it's my dogs, or if it's God Himself, but someone is wanting my attention."

"Wow! That's crazy, Nikki," he says, taking a sip of the wine he brought to the table from the bar area. "I'm not sure if I believe in that kind of stuff, though. It goes against the Greek Orthodox religion."

Then, as if on cue, our server approaches our table and introduces himself. "Hi, my name is Zeni," he says as Theo sits there, visibly shaken by what he's just heard. And frankly, so am I; but I just smile.

"You're really freaking me out, Nikki," Theo says. "If I didn't know better, I'd think you were a witch," I chuckle, realizing Theo is living very much inside a spiritual box. Although admittedly, I'm still a babe in the spiritual woods, trying to figure out where all these signs and synchronicities are coming from.

A couple of weeks later, Theo and I go out to dinner again. When we arrive at the restaurant, he hands his keys to the valet. As we enter the restaurant, he says, "You know, if something like our last date happens again tonight, I'm really going to think you're a witch. No kidding, I may not take you out again."

Sure enough, when the server stops at our table to take our drink order, I notice that her necktie is covered with tiny colored frogs. *It can't be*, I think, reaching for the tie and inspecting it. "Are those frogs on your tie?" I ask, amazed by what I'm seeing.

"They sure are," she replies with a smile.

"That's so cool. I'm actually working on a series called *The Toad Chronicles*. I love when I get confirmation that I'm on the right track."

Theo then proceeds to ask her if the tie is something all the servers wear or if it's her own personal tie. She says, "No, I'm the only one. This is a tie someone gave me a few years ago."

For a minute, I think that Theo is going to up and walk out of the restaurant, freaked out by the thought that I might actually be a witch, but he remains seated.

The synchronicities, however, don't stop there. After the server brings us a piece of key lime pie to share, I excuse myself and head to the lady's room. While I'm gone, I later learn that the server hands Theo one of her business cards (to give to me). She asks him to please notify her when I launch *The Toad Chronicles* series because she's intrigued by my ideas.

When she brings us our check, I thank her for her card. I assure her that I will call her once I'm further along with my projects. She asks me my name and I tell her, "Nikki Karis." Without missing a beat, she replies, "Oh my gosh! I met your dad twenty-six years ago. I was dating Henry Mazza. We came to your brother's house for a Christmas party. Your dad left such an impression on me. I'll never forget him."

Theo is now gripping the edge of the booth, his mouth and eyes wide open, obviously flabbergasted by the serendipity of the evening. By the end of the night, the word "witch" has parted from his lips at least a dozen times. I assure him I'm not a witch, but he doesn't appear to be convinced.

"Um, well, thanks for an interesting time, Nikki," he says, walking me to the back gate of my home.

"I guess it was all a little too much for you," I say, readying to open the gate.

"Look, you're a great girl and all, but I don't think I'm ready for this kind of stuff."

"I understand. Thanks again for dinner." I kiss him lightly on the cheek, then open the gate and walk down the breezeway toward the recreation room.

Once inside, I find Picasso lying on the couch. "Hey there, little man, I missed you," I say to him, rubbing his belly as he lets out the cute doggies sounds that he always does. "I don't know exactly what you're doing to me, or how, or if your grandpa upstairs has something to do with it, but it's pretty damn amazing. You better stick by me, okay? It looks like the journey ahead is going to be a lonely one."

Picasso then snuggles in as close as he can to me, his head buried in my lap. As I stroke him up and down his body, I realize that I will never ever be alone again, not with Picasso by my side.

Chapter Twenty-Seven

Over the ensuing weeks, I engage in a lot of introspection, trying to interlace all the bits and pieces of my life into a fabric that makes sense. So much is happening at once, and I'm grappling to understand what it all means. Something incredibly powerful is definitely taking place in my world, as increased signs and synchronicities are appearing on my path, sometimes several in a given week.

Somehow, I've tapped into and connected with a Higher Power, although I'm not exactly sure how this has happened.

Is it God?

My father?

Or is it a higher aspect of myself?

I don't know for sure, but what I do know is that it's providing me with a profound sense of comfort whilst boosting my creative powers. It's like I am following a path toward an unknown destination, and all the signs and synchronicities are clues as to where I'm headed.

During this time, my father is making his spiritual presence known in a pretty miraculous way. Just last night, he came to Martha, a friend of Clare's, wanting to deliver me a message. I don't know why he chose Martha, as I've never spoken with her or met her in person, but he did. Perhaps it's because she's open to receiving messages from spirits residing beyond, where other people are not; or at least, that's what Clare said.

It's a wild story how this all comes about. But early this morning while I'm on my way to the office, Clare calls me on my cellphone. "I know this may sound strange," she says, "but Martha called me late last night. You remember me telling you about her, right?"

"Yeah, yeah, your friend who lives in California. She's been psychic since she was a child."

"That's the one. Well, last year, I told her your dad had died. And this is freaky. But last night, she started smelling Old Spice cologne and vo5 hair cream. For some odd reason, she thought it might be your dad. Did your dad ever use these products?" she asks.

"Oh, my gosh! Yes, he did. Every morning after he showered, he splashed on Old Spice and ran vo5 through his hair," I reply, fondly recalling this memory. "Tell me. Did he say anything to her?"

"Well, he said to tell you to, 'Stop being sad and get out of the closet with all the shoes.'"

"No way!" I exclaim, realizing something truly magnificent is taking place in my world. I've never met Martha, much less spoken with her, so there is absolutely no way she would know this information about my father. I've never told this kind of stuff to anyone, including Clare. But more importantly, I haven't spoken to anyone about the fact I was grieving him yesterday, which was a Sunday, while I was cleaning out my shoe closet.

I hang up the call with Clare and immediately call my mother to share this most amazing tale. "Mom, you're never going to believe this but...," I say to her, before relaying what happened.

"He's been coming to me, too, honey. I see him at night, standing by the side of the bed. He says he misses me but knows it's not my time."

"Of course it's not your time. I need you too much. I'll call you later after work," I say, then hang up the phone.

In some strange and mysterious way, all the signs and synchronicities, and now the message from my father, are providing me with a roadmap of my journey yet to come. I don't exactly know where it is leading me, but I sense the destination once reached will be heaven on Earth.

Intuitively, I also sense that Paulie and Picasso were sent by God to assist me during my journey. I like to think of them as Goddogs, who comfort, guide, and support me, much like someone is chosen to serve as a godparent at a person's baptism. In some way, I guess I am being baptized because I appear to be turning away from my old life and being reborn into a new one.

Like most people, up until now, I've been trapped on the hamster wheel of life. I've been far too busy to stop, reflect, and heal my emotional wounds. The result is that my emotional scars have continued to deepen, trapping me in the past, and not allowing me to move forward into the future. I keep repeating the same cycles, the same mistakes, unaware of how and why they actually started in the first place.

But with Paulie, and now Picasso, I've been forced to look at parts of myself that I've previously ignored—painful traumas that are now being called up for healing. It's not easy to face the darkness, but it's the only way to break those vicious, repetitive cycles.

For instance, when Paulie was living, he reflected a part of myself that had built walls to protect my heart from all the emotional pain I had endured. The same way he ran away from pain, I had built walls to protect myself from pain. In actuality, though, my walls had achieved the opposite effect, as they had caused me to attract the wrong kind of relationships with both men and women alike.

Thanks to Paulie's guidance, though, I now understand that I need to bring my walls down, heal my emotional wounds, and cultivate a healthy love for myself. It certainly won't be an easy task because my scars are deep—and they are plentiful—but I'm committed to doing it.

Picasso, on the other hand, is reflecting many of my internal fears I keep hidden from the external world—fear of abandonment, fear of judgment, and fear of happiness (for the hurt it may bring). And one big fear I'm experiencing right now is that of embracing the new chapter that is unfolding in my life. As awe-inspiring as this journey is at times, it's also incredibly frightening. I find myself slowly climbing outside the box others have constructed for me—the only walls I'm familiar with—not knowing what exists outside of them.

My family, during this time, seems highly concerned by what's transpiring with me. I'm slowly changing, sometimes painfully, and it's not always a pretty process to witness. Statements like, "She's having a meltdown," "I'm concerned about her Salvation," and "she needs serious professional help," are swirling around my family unit, all referencing me and the mysterious process I am undergoing. Of course, since I'm not entirely certain of what's happening with me, I'm unable to assuage their concerns that I'm not just going crazy.

As for Picasso, his fears haven't gotten any better with time. In fact, they seem to have gotten worse, especially after he underwent training. His trainer, like Paulie's trainer, guaranteed all sorts of fancy-schmancy things. Instead, I ended up firing the asshole, fifteen hundred dollars later.

The incident leading up to it totally upset me. During a session at the house, he held Picasso's face down on the floor and turned the dust buster on. He then yelled at him, "No! No!" while pushing his face harder and harder into the tile floor.

Wrong move, buddy. I wasn't about to stand for someone torturing my dog, even if it was in the name of training. So I politely told him to get out of my house and never to return. No one is going to hurt an animal in my presence, especially one of my own.

Anyway, Picasso is now showing signs of doggie agoraphobia, not that the trainer's actions caused it, mind you. He doesn't like being away from home for extended periods because he gets distressed. Getting him to the vet or taking a road trip together can be a stressful chore for both of us.

But that's fine. While often challenging, I'm learning to work around Picasso's issues. I'm adapting my lifestyle to his, instead of demanding too much from him. I allow him to spend his days, keeping a watchful lookout over the estate while feeling the security of being at home. And for this, he rewards me with unending love, forever acting like my protector and always exhibiting the kind of trust that lasts a lifetime.

Trust—that's something that's been missing in my relationships, especially those with men. Through Picasso's guidance, I hope I can learn to trust once again.

Chapter Twenty-Eight

With Picasso beside me, my creativity is flowing non-stop these days. And this is making me feel more optimistic about my life, something I haven't felt in ages.

Professionally, things are also going well, as I am having one of my best financial years ever. I'm still exhausted from working long hours while creating during the middle of the night, but that's okay. I have a dream to fulfill, and sacrifices must be made.

And then it happens, right as I'm gaining momentum and making serious headway out of the box. My life derails again when my self-esteem takes a powerful and painful nosedive. It starts one afternoon in August, when my mother calls me. She wants me to stop by after work to see her. I can always tell from the tone of her voice when she wants to address something important, because she starts the same way: "Now, Nikki..."

When I arrive at her house, she is sitting on the family room couch with a look on her face that tells me she's quite upset. "What's wrong, Mom?" I ask, sitting down next to her.

"Honey, I need to talk to you," she replies.

By her tone, I know what she is referring to, so I say, "Please tell me there isn't more family drama going on."

"Well, your sister came by the house today, and she and I had an argument. She says that I need counseling because I'm not seeing things clearly when it comes to you. She says you're a disgrace to the community and that the whole town talks about you."

"Me? A disgrace?"

"Honey, listen. That's not the worst of it. Cousin Demetri stopped by after she left and told me some things about you."

"Lies, I'm sure, Mom. Now, what did he say? I want to know," I say, slamming my hand down onto the armrest of the couch, as my blood starts to boil.

"Well, he says that men all over town have been coming up to him, saying they've slept with you. Apparently, he has a list with their names on it."

"A list? Well, I'd like to see that list. I hardly have time to pee, much less sleep with every man in this shithole of a town. This is all one big, fabricated lie to break you and me apart. Can't you see that?"

Suddenly, a sharp pain develops in my solar plexus chakra, the energy center in the body related to a person's self-esteem. I feel like I'm back in fifth grade, experiencing the crucifixion all over again. This pulls a deep-seated trigger in me, and I begin to cry. Now, the judgers and jeerers are going after my mother, the one person left in this world who I can count on. If I lose her emotional support, it will devastate me.

"I've always told you that it's your life," she says. "You're old enough to do whatever you want to do. If you've slept with half the town, that's your business."

"Well, I don't want you believing this bullshit. This is really upsetting to me."

"Do you think I need counseling, honey? That's what your sister says. Maybe she's right," she asks, with a pained look on her face.

"Oh my goodness, no, Mom. You're fine."

"Please, do me a favor," she says, her voice pleading. "Apologize to your sister. You're the only one who can make things right."

"Apologize, for what? If anyone is owed an apology, it's me for the horrible things that have been said about me."

"Please, Nikki, just apologize. Do it for me."

I'm confused, not knowing what I should do. My eighty-five-year-old mother wants her family back together again. And while I love her more than anything in this world, she's asking me to compromise myself for the sake of family members who could give two shits about me. More importantly, no one has asked for forgiveness, so I'm not exactly sure what I would accomplish by agreeing to her request or how to go about achieving it.

It's not as though my mother is feeble or infirmed, mind you—quite to the contrary. She's incredibly sharp and looks and acts much younger than her age. People are astonished, when they learn how old she is. Not only does she live on her own, but she keeps her home in immaculate condition, works as the bookkeeper in my law firm, works out with a trainer, drives all over the place on her own, and sells real estate a few days a week. And prior to my father passing, she took care of him as well.

Still, I'm torn between doing what she's asking of me and what feels right for myself. Finally, I respond: "Look, Mom, I love you more than anything, but I can no longer be a peacemaker. I learned that from you, and it hasn't exactly served me well through the years."

"Are you saying there's something wrong with me. Do you think I need help?"

"Mom, no! I just—" I stop myself, not wanting to get into an argument with her. Already the whole distressing incident is starting to drive a wedge between us—and that's the last thing I want to have happen, as I love her so much. "I really need to go. Picasso is home by himself. I love you."

After kissing her on the cheek, I walk out her front door, hop into the Rover, and head for home.

Chapter Twenty-Nine

A few minutes later, I pull into the portico of my home, turn off the engine to the Rover, and head inside the recreation room. It's comforting to live so close to my mother in case she needs something, especially now that she's getting up in years. Although, I dare not say this to her because the last thing she wants is to feel dependent on me or anyone else.

I plop down on the couch in the recreation room, and Picasso instantly snuggles in next to me. "Hey, sweet boy, I've missed you," I say, stroking him up and down his body. He lets out several of his cute doggie sounds in response.

As I sit there, it all sinks in. My sister's painful words, relayed to me by my mother: "She's a disgrace"—are excruciating. Emotional wounds from my younger years begin to resurface, the pain oozing and seeping into my consciousness. I feel unworthy and unlovable all over again.

Sensing something is wrong, Picasso gently licks away my tears. As he does, I contemplate the path my life has taken so far. I don't understand any of it; really, I don't—so many floggings, so much emotional pain—deep, deep scars that never seem to heal and go away fully. I really thought my life was taking a turn for the better, and now this happens.

There must be a lesson to learn from all that's happened to me (and is still happening), but I can't seem to figure out exactly what it is.

Self-love?

Forgiveness?

Remaining true to my dreams?

What I do know is that my life is painfully shifting. An earthquake of emotions is rumbling inside me, putting my outer world into shambles. It's frightening because with my father gone and my mother still grieving, I have nothing and no one to grab onto. Increasingly, I feel a greater sense of separation from my family, friends, even the whole of society. I'm becoming ever more detached from everything and everyone familiar, and my only refuge, the only place where I feel truly safe, is at home with Picasso and my cats.

I didn't ask for this separation to occur. All I've ever wanted to do is climb outside the box and become the person I am meant to be. Everyone is free to stay where they're at. I'm good with that, really. I just want to go where I'm meant to go without any hassles.

Needing someone, anyone, to talk to about what I've been going through, I call Lily, an acquaintance of mine, who is a leader in the spiritual community. Of all people, I know she will be able to help me.

"You're having a spiritual awakening," she says to me over lunch.

"An awakening?"

"Yes, God, Source, Spirit, whatever you wish to call our Creator, has been forcing you to wake up and rise to your Divine potential."

"You mean my purpose for being here, my mission, the reason God dropped me on this planet?"

"That's exactly what I mean. Everything that isn't based in love and in alignment with your Divine purpose is being swept out of your life. This includes toxic family members, relationships, and long-time friends, possibly even your career as a lawyer. God is helping you make room for your birth, or rather rebirth, and ultimate rise into your Divine destiny."

"So that's it, is it? Well, at least I have a name for it now, the process that I've been going through. It sure isn't fun."

"An awakening isn't designed to be fun. It's meant to drop you to your knees, so you can transform and rise back up out of the ashes."

Sitting across the table from her, I try to absorb all that she's telling me. It's a lot to comprehend, especially with my head still swirling from the conversation I had with my mother on Monday.

"Sometimes God comes through your life like a tsunami and in one fell swoop washes everything away," she continues. "Other times, He does it as a slow drip. Whichever way He chooses, consider yourself lucky. Most people never awaken."

"Lucky? I'd rather go back to sleep," I say, then sigh heavily.

"Nikki, I hate to tell you. But once the awakening starts, you can't stop it. The next phase is your transformation and then comes your rise. Like it or not, God is forcing you to step into your Divine destiny. Once you do, it will be a glorious destination. So don't be scared, okay?"

"Well fuck, just fuck. I should have chosen an easier life path, something a little more mainstream," I say, wryly.

"There is nothing mainstream about you, my dear. Enjoy the journey. Very few choose to take it."

I walk away from lunch feeling equally enlightened as frightened. While I have always felt a deep calling to one day help empower others, never in a million years did I envision going through a spiritual shitstorm to get there. This awakening stuff is not to my liking, not one bit at all, especially the part involving a split from family members.

I'm grateful for Lily's insight, though. Without it, I would think I'm going stark-raving mad. I mean, how do I describe to others the feeling of being stripped naked by God? Because that is what it feels like to me—that God is stripping me of everything and everyone I've ever known.

Growing up, my family wasn't inwardly spiritual, turning instead to church dogma for answers and guidance. I am, thus, the first in my family to explore spirituality beyond the confines of organized religion—and the first to recognize there may be *something* more to this life and to God than what is preached at Sunday liturgy.

In the late evening, I decide to do some research about awakenings and come across several articles that describe its symptomology. One article lists something like fifty-one different signs and symptoms. *Oh, good Lord! What have I gotten myself into?* I think, perusing the extensive list, realizing I've already experienced many of them.

There is one symptom, though, which stands out so much it might as well be slapping me in the face: *a desire to break free from restrictive patterns, life-draining jobs, consumptive lifestyles, and toxic people or situations.* I turn off my laptop, realizing the road ahead is going to be a rocky one.

Chapter Thirty

The next week, Demetri has a family gathering at his house. I'm invited and reluctantly attend at my mother's insistence. When I walk into the living room, I acknowledge several family members, who are talking in the kitchen. All decline (in unison) to acknowledge me and simply keep on talking.

Uncomfortable that I'm being ignored, I turn around and start to head for the door. My mother, obviously seeing this, catches up to me first. "Nikki, honey, don't let them bother you. Now get back in there and hold your head high," she says, tightly gripping onto my right upper arm.

"Mom, I'm sorry, but I'm not going to be treated like shit by my own family. I'll call you later tonight, okay?" I say, grabbing her hand and releasing her grip on me, then kissing her goodbye. On my way out the door, I fight back tears until I get inside my car.

Driving home, tears come gushing out, buckets of them. A movie, more like a horror film, starts to play in my head. Frame by frame, painful experiences from my past come rushing into my consciousness—dozens of them flashing at me in rapid, fire succession—the crown of thorns, the hateful pins, the "Oust Nikki" signs, the "boos" during my graduation speech, the words "she's a disgrace" and "whore," all the endless snickers and sneers, and so many other painful incidents that I've endured through the years. I try to stop the movie from playing, but it feels like it's stuck on a horrible repeat loop, bashing me over and over and over again. The pounding is relentless.

As the frames play on, I begin to question whether I am the bad person everyone thinks I am. I mean, I know I'm not perfect—far from it—as I have lots of faults, foibles, and imperfections. Who doesn't?

But if I'm not a bad person, why would all these awful things have happened (and still be happening) to me? Why would my own family ignore me? Why would my own flesh and blood attack me using words like *disgrace* and *whore* to describe me?

I feel like I'm cracking—like I'm not strong enough to fend the family bullies off. Eventually, they will tear me to shreds and win the battle, pulling me back inside their toxic box, unless I'm somehow able to stop them. My anxiety skyrockets, and my self-esteem plummets.

Suddenly, I realize what I must do. I must escape. Yes, that's it—escape. I need to cash out of everything, move someplace different, and start over, putting the painful memories behind me—forever. And to do that, I need to make certain my future is financially secure.

The following Monday, I take a large shareholder distribution from my law firm's operating account and transfer it, along with another large amount from my personal savings account, into an online investment account. I haven't invested in the stock market since that whole financial debacle which happened in 2001, but I've been keeping a dummy account where I practice trading.

Over a three-year-period, I'm showing a 60% return. If I can earn even a 20% return over two years...well, I'm golden. I will be able to quit the practice of law, move to Harbour Island with Picasso and my cats in tow, and begin the next chapter of my life as a writer. It would be a dream come true.

Right as I begin to reinvest in the stock market, though, conflict within my family (centering around me) escalates even more. My mother attempts to rectify the situation but is met with searing allegations about me. The accusations are downright ugly, to say the least. Learning about this, something triggers in me. I immediately want to escape this hellish nightmare now and not two years from now.

To expedite my exit, in October of 2008, I put myself out on margin right as the stock market suffers a huge crash, one of the largest crashes ever. As the stock market declines, along with the value of my trading account, I panic, trading like a mad woman, pumping even more money into the account. It's like I'm throwing my hard-earned money into a bottomless pit without the safety of a trap door. Huge fortunes are wiped out during this crash, including my own.

When the financial carnage finally ends, I find myself at rock bottom once again. My second attempt to escape the box has been foiled. I feel like my whole life has been washed down the drain; only this time, I have no one to blame but myself.

Chapter Thirty-One

Now March 2009, I've finally emerged from my latest financial debacle, ego bruised and bank accounts empty, and I am angry with myself at losing a sheer fortune I had toiled endless hours to make.

"Why do I allow people's opinions of me to mess with my head?" I ask myself one evening with Picasso cuddled in my lap, as I reflect on the financial annihilation I've just endured. "Every time I do, I end up self-sabotaging."

Picasso raises his head and looks at me, his head cocked to one side, like he knows exactly what I am saying. Once again, he senses that something is wrong with me; and again, he is right. I'm tired—physically, spiritually, mentally, and emotionally. Almost daily, it seems like there is some new drama in my life with a painful lesson attached to it.

But why am I being made to learn so many lessons? What is the point to it all?

For the next hour, I sit with Picasso next to me, attempting to find meaning to my latest financial debacle. Analyzing my situation, I say, "Let's see if there are any patterns going on here."

Reflecting, I realize that on both occasions, when I lost huge fortunes, I invested in the market shortly before a huge crash occurred. Hmmm.... bad timing? Or did God orchestrate this timing to teach me an important life lesson? I analyze further.

Well, let's see. Prior to the first market crash, I wanted to escape the legal profession and fulfill my dream of becoming a talk-show host. In reality, I just wanted to escape life, as I had no real plan for achieving that dream.

The second time around, I wanted to escape the dynamics of my family situation and move somewhere else where no one would know me. Again, I had no real plan of how to accomplish that, as my main objective was to simply escape—to run like Paulie used to do as far and fast as I could.

Finally, reason strikes, and I say to myself, "God obviously has other plans for you. He doesn't want you to cash out and escape life, at least not yet. Girl, you're meant to face your demons, learn your life lessons, and help to empower others."

I think back to the day in third grade when I wanted to help Tommy Uphill with his math problem, and our wicked witch of a teacher handed me a big fat U. I knew then that I wanted to help others.

During my sophomore year of high school, I felt the same way. My best friend came to me, pregnant and crying, not knowing how she would tell her devoutly Catholic parents. I wanted to help her solve her dilemma, by helping to empower her.

And then there was Danielle who, during my junior year of high school, tried to blow herself up in a car. She and I were inseparable until she moved to the other coast of Florida after our freshman year.

I vividly recall walking into the kitchen the morning after my high school's homecoming and my mother saying, "Nikki, sit down. There's something I need to tell you... Danielle's been in an accident."

Upon hearing the news, I immediately booked a flight, hopped on a plane, and flew to Miami by myself. When I walked into the burn unit at Jackson Memorial Hospital and saw Danielle wrapped in bandages, screaming from the searing pain, I wanted to run the other way.

But she needed me, so I gathered up the courage and spent the weekend, sitting next to her bed, consoling her. For the next three months, I traveled to Miami every couple of weeks to see her. It was a humbling experience, but one which cemented my desire to help others overcome their challenges.

In any event, it's now time to move forward and get my creative projects off the ground. No more wasting time. I kiss Picasso on the head, put on my big girl panties, and head upstairs to bed.

The next morning, I wake up early and head into the office with Picasso in tow. I'm still working ridiculously long hours, although I recently hired another paralegal to assist with the intake of new personal injury cases. Thank God for Picasso, though, because he keeps me company on lonely weekend days like today.

During the past ten months, he has really matured. He has finally grown into his head and lost his puppy look, replaced by a strikingly handsome physique. His front and hind legs are chiseled like that of a racehorse, and he has almost no body fat. Physically, he is incredibly strong, but he is also highly sensitive emotionally. Many people mistake him for being a badass when, in fact, he's a total mush pot.

I unleash him, fill his bowl with water, and take a seat at my desk.

A few minutes later, as I'm reviewing a legal document, I hear a voice inside my head. *What was that?* I think, looking down at my desktop phone, believing someone may have left the office intercom system on with the radio playing. But the light for the intercom is red, indicating that it's off. Confused, I shake my head and return to my work.

Then it happens again, only this time I realize that it's not really a voice, per se; but words, positive ones, are making noise in my head. *Holy cow! I hope I'm not going crazy,* I think, reaching for a yellow pad and jotting the words down on paper.

For whatever reason, I feel compelled to share these words on social media. I log into my one-and-only account and attempt to post them. But it's the very first thing I've ever posted, so I struggle to figure out how to even make a post.

Finally, the post is ready: "The world is full of doom and gloom—forget about it and live your life to the fullest, as this too shall pass."

Not my most eloquent execution, that's for sure, but these are the exact words that appear in my head. I tap the post button and wait for some responses, but there aren't any. No one responds because I don't have any friends or followers as of yet.

From that day forward, though, positive words continue to randomly pop into my head. It can happen anywhere—while sitting at my desk, taking a shower, driving to work, or hanging out with Picasso. I don't know where they are coming from—be it God, my father, or maybe some higher aspect of myself—but as they come, I continue to post them on my social media account, slowly building a following.

The more that I engage in this creative process, the more the sayings come to me, sometimes as often as three or four a day. It's an amazing experience; and they do get better—more eloquent and polished—as the weeks and months go by.

With my creativity now in high gear, I take stock of my law practice, trying to figure out in what direction to go next. When I first started practicing law, the personal injury market was still fairly wide open. I was able to build my practice from the ground up via pounding the pavement, from referrals, and some limited phone book advertising. Besides that, I also lectured on motor vehicle insurance law a couple of times a year, helping to build my reputation as a knowledgeable lawyer.

Nowadays, every attorney is jumping on the P.I. bandwagon, thinking they can make a quick, easy buck. It's insane, as advertising is popping up everywhere. Fresh-out-of-law-school attorneys with no experience are throwing up a shingle, buying up some ad space, and competing with more experienced lawyers like myself, hoping to cash in on a big settlement.

Personal injury attorneys, at least a vast majority of them, are like an army of caterpillars—all trying to climb to the top of the pillar that's becoming more and more crowded every single day. It's what Yellow, Stripe, and all the other caterpillars were doing in *Hope for the Flowers*. One day, as sure as gravity, the pillar known as the personal injury legal market is going to collapse from the weight of all the lawyers climbing it.

Then two months later, when I'm at my office working on a Saturday, I get the push I finally need to get my creative projects moving forward. It's a beautiful day, and I'm stuck inside perusing a stack of legal documents, some prepared by my staff for my signature and others prepared by opposing counsel which require my review.

Frustrated that I'm chained to my desk yet again on a Saturday, I have a sudden revelation: "Enough of this insanity! I've spent so much time the past several years focused on my law practice that I've neglected my dreams. It's time I shift gears and build a foundation for my creative concepts, so I can escape this insane profession."

With that realization, I push aside the stack of documents and begin to formulate a *real* plan of escape.

Chapter Thirty-Two

Since yesterday's revelatory moment, I've been thinking, long and hard, about my creative projects and the ones I want to focus on. Much internal debate later, I've decided it's time to write book one of *The Toad Chronicles* series, as that's my current plan for escaping the legal profession. It's also part of my dream to help empower others, as I want my series to deliver an inspiring message. As for my dream of becoming a talk show host, I hope my book, once published, will open up doors for me.

To facilitate my plan, I book a flight to Harbour Island, departing two weeks from yesterday, and reserve a room at the Bahamas House, my favorite inn on the island. Thankfully, a trial scheduled for that week has been postponed, opening a week-long slot on my calendar.

I also call a local boarding facility and reserve a spot for Picasso for when I'm away. While I hate boarding him, I have no other option at the moment, as I haven't yet found an in-home sitter who I trust. And he's far too energetic for my mother to handle on her own.

Two weeks later, I land at the North Eleuthera Airport, hail a taxi, and take a tender boat over to the Harbour Island dock. Bags in hands, raring to go, I see a familiar face who offers me a ride.

"Hey, Nikki, hop on my golf cart," Marcus says. "I'll take you to where you need to go. Where are you staying?"

"It's so good to see you, Marcus. I'm staying at the Bahama House," I reply, loading my bags onto the back of his golf cart. In my bags, I've packed a couple of bikinis, several sundresses, a half-dozen pairs of shoes, two light wraps for the evenings, make-up, jewelry, some other incidentals, and my precious laptop. I never go anywhere without it these days, as inspiration tends to strike when I least expect it to.

Marcus drops me off at the inn shortly after noon. "Thanks for the ride. I hope to see you around," I say, grabbing my bags off the back of the cart. I wave to Marcus, then head inside the gate to the inn.

John, the proprietor of the inn, has left the door to my room unlocked, since he's out fishing with some of his friends. I unpack my bags, change into a comfortable sundress, and power on my laptop, anxious to dive into writing. Sitting on the bed, staring at my laptop screen, I wait for inspiration to strike, but nothing happens—nothing, nada, not even a flicker.

"Ugh!" I exclaim. I then walk outside barefoot into the courtyard, seeking to ground myself in Mother Earth, hoping it will help to get my creative juices flowing.

A few minutes later, feeling recharged, I return to my room and plop back down on the bed. I stare at the screen for a second time, waiting for inspiration to well up inside of me. But once again, there's nothing. Not one single word comes to mind. "The beach, that's what I need. That should spawn my creativity," I say to my myself, powering off my laptop.

I throw on a bikini and a coverup, add a pair of my favorite rhinestone-studded flip-flops and a straw hat with wide-rimmed sunglasses, and out the door I go. Next door to the inn, there's a golf cart rental shop, so I stop in and rent a two-seater cart. I then purchase some cold bottles of water and a bag of plantains from the food market across the street.

Armed and ready to go, I drive the cart through the island's narrow cobblestone streets toward the famous pink sand beach. It's an exceptionally beautiful day, with not a single cloud in the sky. It's just what the inspiration doctor ordered; or so, I hope.

For the next two hours, I swim and lie on my towel, soaking up some much needed vitamin D. When I'm done, I grab a fresh conch salad from a take-out stand and head back to my room. This time, when I power on my laptop, *voilà*! The inspiration doctor has miraculously cured me, as all creative blocks have been removed

I then spend the next five days, writing and rewriting the introduction. Each afternoon, I head to the beach and spend a few hours in the sun, waiting for the next wave of creativity to strike which, thankfully, it does.

The finished introduction is adequate, certainly not award-winning material, but it's a decent start to the book. I haven't written creatively in years, so I pat myself on the back for a job well done.

Before I leave the island, I promise myself that I will devote a certain portion of every day to writing. No easy task, mind you, given all my other responsibilities, but I'm up for the challenge because this is the path of escape that I've chosen to take.

When I arrive home, I settle into a routine, toggling between my work responsibilities and writing. Within a few weeks, though, I begin showing signs of physical exhaustion. It's becoming harder and harder to get out of bed in the morning, much less get through a full day dealing with the demands of my busy law practice while working on my book in the middle of the night.

Then one morning in early June 2009, I wake up feeling like a knife is cutting me across the throat. I try to get out of bed but lack the strength to pull myself up.

"Come on, you can do it, one foot in front of the other," I tell myself, but it doesn't work. My feet feel like they're weighted down with lead, and I fall back into bed.

Clearly, my body needs rest. If I don't get some soon, I'm going to be in really big trouble. I take Picasso downstairs to use the bathroom, then phone my office and tell my assistants that I'm not coming in today. For the remainder of the day, I sleep with Picasso beside me. He doesn't make a sound, obviously sensing my need to rest.

Finally, around six o'clock that night, I drag myself downstairs to the recreation room to feed him and give him another potty break. I feel bad, but it's all I can do right now. Thinking of my poor cats, I slowly make my way to the upstairs apartment, feed them, and scoop out their litter boxes. I'm thoroughly exhausted, by the end of it.

The next morning, I struggle for a second time to get out of bed. Again, I can't do it. I've never felt such extreme exhaustion in my entire life. It's like my body won't respond to my brain's request to get moving. Deep inside, I'm now panicking because I've never suffered with health issues, not ever, and I never ever miss a day of work. I fall back into bed and sleep for the rest of the day.

When I finally get out of bed later in the day, I head into the bathroom and look into the mirror. I don't even recognize myself. My skin is sallow, my hair is dry and brittle, and my eyes are sunken. I look like death warmed over. At this point, I'm super scared. Tears stream down my face because I'm worried about my potential fate as well as Picasso's. Who will take care of him, if I die?

Staring at my reflection in the mirror, I say, "Nikki, you're going to die young, if you don't do something about this situation. It's time to take control of your health."

Upon hearing my pained words, Picasso wanders into the bathroom. I look down, and he cocks his head to the side, like he understands exactly what I'm going through. We both know this is my wake-up call. Something has to give—and fast! Otherwise, I'm not going to live long enough to see my dreams fulfilled.

I go back to bed, power on my laptop, and begin researching my symptoms. Intuitively, I'm drawn to an online nutritionist who, at one time, suffered from intestinal candida, the malady I believe is gripping me. Like myself, she had a long history of antibiotic use before undergoing a self-healing. Her story resonates with me, so I immediately commence with her candida-free diet, consisting of grass-fed red meat, green vegetables, and a handful of berries, along with a regime of oregano oil and about a dozen different vitamins.

Because the diet is time-consuming to shop for and prepare, I hire a young man named "Adam" to assist me part-time, running errands, doing some light housekeeping and shopping, and helping to care for Picasso. He is an absolute God-send because he helps to relieve some of my responsibilities and, in turn, my stress.

I start the diet about a month before I am set to co-counsel a large personal injury trial which turns out to be a really bad move. When the trial starts, I'm utterly miserable and have a tough time sitting still. The toxins are delivering a searing pain into my shoulders while exiting my body. I try to concentrate on the trial, but it's difficult because the pain is almost unbearable. Ultimately, though, the jury comes back with a sizable verdict for our client, thanks to the efforts of my co-counsel.

With the trial now over, I decide to intensify my diet and move the healing process along more quickly. I add to my morning regime a frothy, iced drink recommended by the nutritionist consisting of three raw eggs, four tablespoons coconut oil, two tablespoons whole butter, nutmeg, cinnamon, cardamom, and Stevia. Disgusting sounding, I know, but the drink is incredibly detoxifying.

This proves to be another ill-fated decision, though, as I push the detoxification way faster than I should, overwhelming my body in the process. I end up having to slow things down, so that I can continue functioning throughout my day.

For the next couple of months, I continue to detoxify, proceeding slower than before. Years of chemicals, vaccine adjuvants, toxins, and other gunk stored in my organs and cells are brought to the surface. My face breaks out in huge welts, and I lose sixteen pounds in a flash. People start whispering that I look like I have cancer.

At this point, I'm clearly in a battle with myself. One part of me is worried, believing I should seek the opinion of a medical doctor, while the other part of me intuitively feels I'm on the right path with my healing. But because I've relied on the advice and opinions of others all my life—and look where it's gotten me—I feel the need to forego seeking medical advice and proceed forward on my own.

Still, I'm nervous because I have no one, absolutely no one, close to me to talk to about this kind of stuff. None of my family members or close friends have experienced anything even remotely akin to a spiritual awakening, much less tried to heal themselves holistically.

Once again, I go online and conduct some research. That's when I learn that homeopathic medicine works by healing the body from the inside out—first the organs, next the joints, then ultimately the skin. It retraces all prior illnesses (without manifesting the actual symptoms) by mentally calling them up so they can be addressed, healed, and released for good. Satisfied with the results of my research, I decide to rely on my instincts and forge on.

The physical and emotional purging continues, dredging up deep-rooted emotions and fears, some completely irrational. At one point, I actually think that I might have some form of latent MD, MS, cancer, you name it, whatever my mind conjures up in the whim of the moment, but I remain strong and committed to my path of healing. I know it's something I absolutely must do, if I wish to take my health and ultimately, my life back into my own hands.

Chapter Thirty-Three

Despite feeling exhausted from detoxing, something miraculous is occurring with me. The more I slough off old, outdated ways of thinking, feeling, and being, the more my channels of creative expression are opening up. Slowly, my book is writing itself, as words flow effortlessly from my subconscious into the manuscript, and my inspiring messages continue to channel to me, often several a day.

Signs and synchronicities are also appearing in my path again. Only this time, they are much more abundant than on previous occasions. Toads, both real and manufactured, are leaping up everywhere—on billboards and t-shirts, in my driveway, and many places I venture to—providing me strong confirmation that I'm on the right track with the ideas for my book series.

Just the other night, for example, I was out to dinner with Tara, a business acquaintance, who was asking about my series. As I was telling her about the series, a man walked by the window of the restaurant where we were sitting, wearing a t-shirt with three toads and the words, "Toadily Wasted," printed on the front.

We both burst out laughing, because of the timing of it. For me, though, the timing was too impeccable for it to be sheer coincidence, although that's what Tara thought it was—a coincidence, nothing more. But Tara isn't the least bit spiritual, so I refuse to let her burst my bubble.

Lily told me this would happen. She said once I started cleaning out all the junk and gunk trapped inside my cellular structure, I would begin to reconnect with Source (God, as I call this Source). God would then help to guide me toward my Divine mission via signs, synchronicities, and number sequences, although I have yet to experience the number thing as of yet.

So I guess that's what I'm doing right now—working toward stepping into my Divine mission—because the signs and synchronicities are becoming more plentiful, especially when I'm on Harbour Island, where I travel every three months or so to write.

Actually, I'm on the island right now, sitting at Valentine's Marina, working on my book, while having an early dinner. Paul, a friend of mine, whom I met two trips ago, is sitting with his girlfriend at a table next to mine. We're chatting about my new favorite subject—dogs.

Paul says to me, "Have you seen those cute puppies on the way to Romora Bay?"

"Oh, gosh, Paul, please don't tell me about them. Otherwise, I'll have to stop by and take a look. And if I do, I'll be doomed," I say, secretly wanting to know the puppies' location.

Well, I hate to be predictable. But next thing you know, after I finish eating and pay my bill, I jump into my golf cart and head to see the puppies. Chuckling at my request, Paul has graciously given me directions to the puppies' whereabouts. He says they are owned by a man named Donny Sawyer.

"Be forewarned, though," Paul says, after explaining where the house is located. "The conditions they are living in are pretty subpar."

To my horror, when I arrive, I find a momma dog and her puppies living in squalor, with their only refuge from the elements being under a partially rusted-out car. The puppies, five in total, appear to be about seven to eight weeks old. A couple of them are wandering dangerously close to the road, so I corral them and devise a makeshift pen to keep them safe. One of the puppies almost falls into a huge garbage pit on the premises, but I grab him just in time and put him inside the pen.

Peering down at the puppies, I fall in love with one of them, a white one with butterscotch-colored markings, and decide I want to adopt her. Actually, I love the entire family, momma dog included, but I know that I can only manage one new puppy at this time. I knock on the door, wanting to talk with Mr. Sawyer about adopting the puppy, but no one is home.

"Damn it!" I exclaim, looking around, trying to figure out what to do next. I know I can't just take the puppy. Besides, I want to speak with Mr. Sawyer and make sure the momma dog and the other puppies will be taken care of.

I need to get back my writing, though. So before I depart, I say to the adorable family of mutts, "Well, sweet babies, I hate to leave you in these conditions, but I have to go. Momma, you take care of your babies. I'll be back tomorrow."

At eight o'clock the next morning, I return to the house and find the puppies outside their makeshift pen. I notice that a white one with chocolate-brown markings is off by herself. She is so frail and weak that she topples over onto her face, as she tries to walk. Immediately, I pick her up and cuddle her, wanting her to feel safe. She is shaking in my hands, but eventually calms down.

"Oh my, little one. You're going to die unless someone rescues you," I say before realizing that "someone" will be me. *This is the puppy I am meant to save*, I think, knocking on the once again door, hoping Mr. Sawyer will be home. Again, no one answers.

Frustrated, and seeing the sad state of health the puppy is in, I decide to take her because I'm certain she will die without my intervention. Then as I'm stepping up into the golf cart, a man appears from the house. "Miss, can I help you?" he says.

"Yes, are you Mr. Sawyer?" I ask him, embarking from the golf cart and walking toward him with the puppy in my arms.

"I sure am. What can I do for ya?"

"I'm wanting to adopt this puppy. She is very sick, and I want to bring her back to Florida for medical treatment." I hold my breath waiting for his response.

"That'll be fine," he finally says. "You know, she's one of my favorites. Her legs were rolled over by that ol' car over there. I spent a lot of hours working with her, gettin' her to walk again."

"Aww, that's so kind of you," I say, trying not to judge the man for the conditions the dogs are living in. "How about the other puppies and the momma? What will happen to them?"

"Oh, I've got homes for all of them. The one you're holding, well, I was gonna keep her for myself but you seem like a nice lady. How 'bout givin' me fifty dollars, and she'll be yours?"

"Fair enough. I'll bring the money to you this afternoon, if that's all right. I'm also going to bring you a bag of dog food for the others."

"That's fine. If I'm not here, leave the money and the food with George, the Haitian man who works for me."

"I will. Thank you, Mr. Sawyer. I hope you have a good day."

"You too, ma'am."

I drive away with the puppy cradled even closer in my arms. "You're safe now, little one. Never again will you go hungry, not as long as I'm around," I say, stroking her head.

As I drive away from Mr. Sawyer's place, tears stream down, the poisons and toxins inside my body continuing to wash away. I think about the fate of the puppy's momma and siblings, hoping one day soon, I'm able to do more to help the voiceless animals of this world.

Chapter Thirty-Four

Halloween Day 2009 proves to be quite memorable because I've now adopted my second dog (the third dog I've ever owned), and I'm over the moon to be adding another member to my family.

Holding the malnourished puppy in my arms, I head toward my room at Valentine's Marina. En route, I stop at one of the food markets, where I buy two cans of Purina Puppy Chow and a bottle of Joy, as the puppy is in desperate need of a sudsy bath and thorough defleaing. I'm not even sure if the hotel allows dogs in the room, much less mangy rescued ones, but I don't care because the puppy is on the verge of death. There is no vet clinic on the island, so I remain her only salvation.

Arriving at my room, I place the puppy in the deep tub and step inside of it. With all the grime and fleas embedded in her coat, it takes three washings to do the job. I use my tweezers and excise as many of the remaining fleas I can, but it's a daunting task as she's still covered in them.

The more fleas I remove from her body, though, the more alert she becomes, so I forge on—picking, picking, picking. By the time I'm done, the tub, made of white ceramic, is so covered with tiny black flea carcasses that it looks like the dark bottom of a pond.

After a brisk drying and fluffing, I wrap the puppy inside a clean towel and lay her in the bed next to me. She is so thoroughly exhausted that she sleeps the entire time I work on my book.

When she wakes an hour later, she starts yapping at the top of her lungs. She's obviously hungry, so I mix her a porridge of puppy food and water which she laps up voraciously. Rather than feeling worried, I am thrilled because I got to her just in time. Clearly approaching starvation, it's doubtful she would have survived another couple of days.

A few hours later, I return to Mr. Sawyer's place, leave the money and bag of food with George, and pray that the momma and other puppies will find good homes. I can't save all the maltreated puppies in the world, at least not today.

My next challenge is to find a way to get the puppy to Florida. The vet only comes to the island once every two weeks, so I can't get the necessary paperwork to fly her until the vet's next visit. Thankfully, after running around the island knocking on doors begging and pleading with people, I find a woman who does rescue on the island. She agrees to foster the puppy, take her to the vet, and fly her to Ft. Lauderdale in a couple of weeks.

That night, I name the puppy Izzie, short for Isabella, because I've always wanted a daughter by that name. Granted, Izzie has four legs, as opposed to two, but quickly I consider her my spiritual flesh and blood as if she were my human daughter.

Two days later, I drop Izzie off at the foster's house, along with a bag of food and a blanket I bought for her at a local store, then bid her a tearful farewell. Because the foster has a party going on, several kids rush in to dote on Izzie. Feeling she will be well cared for in my absence, I heave a sigh of relief, then rush out the door because I'm running late for my flight home to Florida.

Three weeks later, Izzie is set to arrive at noon at the Ft. Lauderdale Executive Airport and pass through customs. My mother and I make the four-hour drive to the airport to pick her up. While I go inside the airport to find the foster, my mother waits inside the car.

Immediately, I spot the foster, coming through customs with Izzie, now an official U.S. dog citizen, who is sitting inside the top of the foster's tote bag. It's the cutest thing I've ever seen—Izzie sitting in that tote bag, all smiles and wiggles. And already she's grown quite a bit since I last saw her, proving what a little food will do for a malnourished puppy.

"Oh, wow! She's gotten so big," I say to the foster as she hands me Izzie.

"Your girl loves to eat. That's for sure."

"I can't thank you enough for taking care of her."

After the foster leaves us, I sit in the lobby for a few minutes doting on Izzie, hardly believing my fate. I am overjoyed that my little girl is safe in Florida, ready for our life together to begin.

Chapter Thirty Five

When you've been down for so long, it's empowering to wake up in the morning to a hormonal surge of pleasure even if only fleeting. Maybe I feel good today because the sun is peeking through the guesthouse window, casting warmth across my bed. Or maybe, it's because my body is telling me that I'm well on the road to recovery.

I pull back the bed covers and swing my bare feet to the floor, yawning and stretching my arms at the sunshine of the day. *Gosh! I feel so much better this morning, better than I have felt in months*, I think walking out of the guest house into the backyard.

Barefoot, I begin grounding in precious Mother Earth, wiggling my toes and feeling her energy run through my body. The grass is still wet and cold from the morning dew, but it feels good beneath my feet.

As I stand there, I see Picasso and Izzie staring at me through the glass of the French doors leading into the recreation room. Their heads are cocked to the side, no doubt wondering why I'm not attending to their every need the moment I start moving.

"Be right there, babies," I holler, watching them run to another set of doors to get my attention.

This puts an enormous smile on my face, reminding me of the day that I rescued Izzie, a little over four months ago. Despite her terrible state at the time, she has since transformed into the most beautiful dog ever, donning a gorgeous white speckled coat which reminds me of a spotted owl and the coolest brown markings around her eyes that look like a mask.

She also has a huge, round patch of brown fur on her back that looks like a bullseye.

It's been inspiring to watch her overcome her challenges, something I'm forever trying to do it my own life. I once read castaway dogs like Izzie feel a sense of hopelessness—until they are saved, that is. I, too, felt a sense of hopelessness at the time I rescued Izzie because I was in the middle of a powerful detox that had dropped me to my knees. But the detox seems to have worked fabulously, as I'm feeling better than ever before.

Apparently, detoxing has also changed my appearance; and quite markedly, as several friends have genuinely commented that I look so much younger these days. One friend, a crazy, loveable woman, who cusses like a sailor and smokes like a fiend, insists that I've had a facelift. "Oh, honey, it can't just be detoxing," she says to me one afternoon.

I assure her that no surgery has been involved, as she stretchers her face in contemplation. "Girl, it's just clean living," I joke, and we both have a loud laugh as she takes another drag on her cigarette.

You know, there's something incredibly liberating about taking your health into your own hands. When I finally trusted my instincts and forged on with the detox, despite my fears, it worked—and more. It had a positive impact on my entire life—a domino effect as it were.

And right now, I'm feeling better than I've felt in years, and definitely a lot more empowered. After nearly being snuffed out, my inner light is starting to shine once again. Sure, admittedly, I'm still a work in progress, as I've got a long way to go to turning that light completely back on—but I'm ever so slowly coming back to life.

Every day, another layer of the onion gets peeled back, allowing more of my innate radiance to sparkle. It's like every single cell of me is being called up for examination, whereupon it is either jettisoned from my body or made to change for the good. It's a formidable task, but the rewards are proving to be immeasurable.

I'm also beginning to question more the essence of life and the magical world opening up around me. That's what happens when darkness lifts, especially darkness flung over by negative narrative and misguided pressure to conform. Now, I want to investigate and see the world through my own lens versus the lens constructed by others.

For example, one evening, I quizzically ask myself, "Are the world's financial markets manipulated to benefit the ultra-rich?" It's a view I had previously refused to embrace but am now much more opened to.

"Does religion hide the truth about God and where we originated from?" I question one day, sitting in a church pew at St. Michael's Shrine, where I often go to light a candle and say a prayer.

"Who or what really caused the 9/11 disaster?" I really want to know the truth because the narrative given by the mainstream media doesn't sit right with me, nor has it since the day that horrible event occurred.

It's like waking up one day in a world of zero gravity. Everything I once believed to be true, my entire foundation, now appears to be false. The veils of illusion are being brought down, one by one, and this is radically changing my view of the world. I'm now finding truth from my own internal knowledge and connection with God versus relying upon narrative propagated by others which is often manipulated to serve an ulterior purpose.

Not too long ago, I read about this happening, about things looking and feeling different in the world once an awakening began. A couple of on-line articles talked about being "awakened" as realizing that much of what is portrayed by our governments, religious organizations, educational systems, and the media is highly misleading propaganda or downright lies, told to keep people impoverished, disempowered, and divided from each other and, in turn, separated from God.

That's a hard pill to swallow. But the more I awaken, the more I am beginning to see a strong element of truth to it. Other than Lily, though, I

Nikki Karis

really can't talk to anyone about this kind of stuff because most people will think I'm crazy (especially those who think I'm already crazy). They are too indoctrinated by the mainstream media and the government narrative to think any different.

Anyway, it doesn't matter what other people think about what's going on in the world—or what they think of me, for that matter. The only thing that's important is my own internal belief system which is growing stronger as my awakening continues. Besides, I've got Picasso and Izzie now, and they think I'm pretty damn cool. We are all really beginning to shine together—a super bonded trio, we are.

Every day, these two beautiful souls teach me something new about myself and help me love myself unconditionally. Admittedly, I still have a long way to go to heal all my inner wounds, but I'm slowly making progress. One wound that I still have to heal, or at least come to peace with, is the one with my family, but that's going to take a while as the hurt runs deep.

"Hi, babies," I say to Picasso and Izzie, after opening the door to the recreation room. "Did you sleep okay?"

Izzie circles me several times, rubbing up against me and weaving in and out between my legs in her signature way. Picasso, meanwhile, sits eagerly in front of me, whining and waiting for me to pet him. I reach down and give them both vigorous, loving rubs.

"I love you both so much. You are both so incredibly cool," I say, opening the refrigerator and grabbing some cold ginger tea.

With my glass of tea in hand, I sit down on the massive leather sectional couch I purchased about a month ago, so all of us could be comfortable together. Picasso and Izzie jump into their places—Picasso stage left, Izzie stage right. Already the new couch is marred from their nails. But who cares? Material stuff can be replaced.

Surveying the couch, I say, "Hmm... I wonder how many more rescue dogs I could fit on this couch? Quite a few, by the size of it. Maybe I should become the Goddogger," I chuckle, then take several sips of my tea, stopping to rub Picasso and Izzie in between.

"Crud!" I suddenly exclaim. Time is escaping me. I look at the calendar on my cellphone and am reminded that I have another fairly busy day ahead of me: a court hearing at nine o'clock, a lunch meeting at noon, a short doctor's deposition via phone at 2:00 p.m., and a few phone conferences. That's actually not too bad. But before the day is through, who knows what else will rain down on me.

I think I'll just sit here for a few more minutes and enjoy the ones I love. This whole dog parenting thing is truly filling a void in my life, I think, sipping on my tea.

You know, I've never had human children, never even had the opportunity to think about it because I haven't yet met that special someone. And the thought of being a single parent isn't something that appeals to me. So dog children it is for me, at least for now.

A former friend once told me that if I really wanted children, I would have them regardless of my circumstances, but she really didn't understand me. In my opinion, proper consideration should be given to someone's circumstances before deciding to have children; and for me, the timing just hasn't been right. I want to be available for my child, and I want the child's father actively involved in our lives as well.

That said, love is elusive, and I haven't yet found my Stripe. Maybe one day, I will give up on the idea of finding him and adopt some children on my own. But for now, I'm happy being a dog parent, although I must admit that it's infinitely more challenging having two dogs than one.

Picasso and Izzie are like a typical brother and sister, loving each other one minute and hating each other the next, although they've formed quite a bond. And Picasso, well, he gets a little miffed—more like jealous, I presume—when Izzie gets attention before he does. But he quickly adjusts, realizing he's got a little sister to take care of.

There was this one time, though, when he was quite naughty. He dug a huge hole under the big oak tree and watched Izzie fall into it. Once she was inside, he started kicking dirt into the hole using his hind legs. Thankfully, I was close by to rescue Izzie before any harm had befallen her.

I call the holes "Picasso's man caves," because he disappears inside of them for hours at a time. He digs them between the monster ferns planted around the oak tree, so he has just the right amount of shade from the Florida sun. So smart, he is!

And Izzie, well, she's incredibly smart, too. She breezed through potty training and learned how to sit, after just a few lessons. But she is far more laid back than Picasso who, in many ways, is like me—always a little on edge and not being able to relax and enjoy life to the fullest.

It must be close to 7:00 a.m. because I hear Adam pulling into the portico by the back gate. He's now working for me full-time as my personal assistant and caring for Picasso and Izzie while I'm at work. Not only does he feed them, but he plays with them and takes them on walks (so spoiled, they are). I give Picasso and Izzie one last good rub down, then head upstairs to get ready for court.

Chapter Thirty-Six

Today is a rare chilly morning, providing a welcomed reprieve from the typically hot humid days of the Florida gulf coast. And right now, I'm on my way to court to see Judge Smocket, who I haven't seen in a couple of months. The morning's hearing is on Mrs. Desuth's case and pertains to some discovery issues over which me and the tobacco attorneys are arguing in preparation for an eventual trial.

Four months ago, I brought experienced co-counsel on board because a small firm like mine just can't keep up with the demands of a full-on tobacco trial. Of course, I also wanted to free up some time to pursue my dreams and write book one of my *The Toad Chronicles* series—a win-win, if everything turns out as planned.

With co-counsel assisting me, attorney's fees will be split 50/50, whereas before I was to earn all of the fees. But the upside is that I now have the assistance of other lawyers, something I've needed for a very long time. Nonetheless, the hearing is one that I'm handling on my own.

If I were really honest with the Universe, what I wouldn't give to just kiss this case totally goodbye—client, fees, and all. It's dragging on way longer than expected and costing me a fortune to litigate. But I have too much time and money invested to quit now, so onward I march to see Billy Boy and his entourage of stiffs.

En route to the courthouse, I listen to the voice messages on my cellphone. There's one from my mother, and her voice is quivering. "Nikki, please give me a call. I really need to talk to you."

"Now what?" I say to myself, tapping my foot nervously on the floorboard at the next red light. I hope it's not more family drama because I've had enough of it to last ten lifetimes.

You know, the more I set boundaries, the angrier certain family members, friends, even some employees, seem to get with me. The old, disempowered Nikki over whom everyone ran roughshod is fading away, slowly replaced by a more empowered one—and this has been rankling people.

Looking back, I can't believe that I allowed people to walk all over me for so long. I know it had to do with my poor self-esteem which I'm working to rebuild, but there's no little pill that fixes years of emotional trauma. It's a slow upward trajectory with more than an occasional setback.

I play my mother's message back several times and decide that I need to call her back now because her tone has me worried. After several rings, she answers. I start right in: "Mom, I've had it. You tell whoever it is that's giving you a hard time about me to stop, just stop."

For a long moment, there is nothing but silence. Then I hear her sniffling. "I'm sorry, Mom. I didn't mean to lose my temper. It's just—"

She sniffles again. "Mom, are you okay?" I ask.

"I was just calling to tell you that Harry died. He and his wife used to double-date with me and your father," she replies.

"Oh, no, Mom, of course I remember Harry. Sorry, I'm so sorry. I thought something went on with the family again. Oh, gosh, when did it happen?" So she tells me, and I console her until I pull into the courthouse parking lot, where I gently say goodbye.

"Your home away from home," I say half-heartedly, checking my face in the rearview mirror. I hop out of the Rover and race inside the courthouse, where I wait for the clerk to call my case.

Sitting there, I think about my parents, who were married almost sixty-two years when my father passed away. They were best friends, lovers, and partners in their journey of life. Sure, they argued from time to time. What couple doesn't? But they managed to get through the good times and the bad—together, for better or worse—and to love one another as the saying goes, "Until death do us part."

I so wish I could find someone to share my life with—my triumphs, my struggles, my ups, and my downs. Life has been a lonely journey, especially with all my friends being married and having children.

People tell me that I'm too picky. They say, "Nikki, there are tons of men out there who would marry you, if you would just settle." Oh, that word—*settle*. It sends my heart into palpitations from the mere thought of marrying someone who isn't absolutely the one for me.

You know, I've never had a relationship that's lasted longer than twenty months. I also haven't lived with anyone or had a marriage proposal— unless you count Manuel, the Greek, who threw a four-carat diamond ring at me weeks after I broke up with him.

Before Manuel showed up with the ring, he went by my parents' house (a few days earlier). I vividly recall when my mother called me and said, "Manuel is here talking with your father. Why don't you stop by the house?"

"I can't," I replied. "I'm headed to the movies with my friend, Doug."

Then it hit me like a bolt of lightning. "Oh, my god, Mom! Is he asking Dad for permission to marry me?"

"Uh, huh, well—"

"Sorry, Mom, I love you and Dad, but I don't want to see that jerk ever again, not with the way he has treated me. You're on your own."

The next day, my mother called me and relayed what happened, after we talked on the phone. My father had told Manuel, "Son, you don't know the first thing about what makes my daughter tick. It's obviously her decision. But on the off chance she does say yes to you, I want you to know that I won't give you a dowry. I'll be giving you an educated woman, my daughter, and that's enough."

Yes, score one for my pops! He was always so wise. And he really got me, even though he was somewhat of an older father when I was born (being forty-seven and all). He never pushed the idea of marriage on me, like so many Greek fathers do to their daughters. My father's motto: educate your daughters and give them the freedom of choice.

Anyway, shortly after I shook Manuel from my life, a friend and I went to see a lady who claimed she could foretell a person's future from visions sent to her by God. My friend had seen her several times before and thought she was amazingly gifted. So, I thought, *Why not give it a try?*

Well, after saying the Lord's prayer with her, she began telling me all sorts of things about myself—things she could never know since I'd never met her before. She also told me that, in the future, there would be a man with blonde hair and blue eyes in my life who would later become my husband. But the part that really stuck with me was that she saw our relationship as being up in the heavens, as being blessed by God. She said she'd never seen anything like it before.

So that's what I've been looking for all these years—a man with whom our relationship is blessed by God. I'm not exactly sure what that means, of course. All I know is that I will know when, and if, it happens whether the man has blonde hair and blue eyes or not.

Although, admittedly, I still have a lot of work to do to figure out who exactly God is. I know what my Greek Orthodox religion taught me about God when I was growing up. In Sunday school, which I attended until I was twelve years old, there were all those picture books, depicting God as a man sitting on a throne high up in the Heavens.

But this, and so much else that I've heard and read about God through the years, doesn't comport with my idea of who or what God actually is. The idea that there is a separate geographic location where God lives doesn't make sense to me because He feels far more powerful and encompassing—like an energy force which is part of everything and everyone. But I can't say for sure if this is what I actually believe, since I'm still investigating all of it.

What I do know is I don't want to be in this courtroom right now, battling a behemoth tobacco company on a discovery motion. Being a published author and inspirational speaker (and making a good living at it as well) is my dream. I want to travel the world empowering others, via the written and spoken word, not drain my life force energy battling evil.

"Desuth versus Southern Tobacco," the Clerk announces. After standing, I walk through the wooden gate and head toward the table where plaintiff's counsel sits, carrying my briefcase and a huge, red rope file along with me.

"I object!" I want to scream but don't. The last thing I want (or need) is to get reported to the Florida Bar Association and be disbarred because I don't have another income stream in place. That would be a really stupid, stupid move on my part.

But if I'm honest with myself, truly honest, I will admit that I've somehow lost my soul being an attorney all these years. I just wish I knew where to find it again—my soul that is. Maybe that's what my Goddogs, Picasso and Izzie, will help me do. I sit down at the plaintiff's table and mentally prepare myself for the pointless battle that is about to ensue.

Chapter Thirty-Seven

Now, a month or so later (April 19, 2010, to be exact), I'm celebrating the eleventh anniversary of the opening of my law firm. What a journey it has been, building a company from the ground up through blood, sweat, and tears. And although I'm finally starting to appreciate just how successful I've been, I must concede that it has come with a price—a feeling that I've foregone a greater purpose in life.

Today is also a little over three years since my father passed away, and I miss him like it was yesterday. He is still coming to Martha, once every couple of months or so, delivering me messages of consolation and hope as if he were still living. These messages give me some sense of solace, despite my ever-present feeling of grief.

Two days ago, Clare called me when I was on my way to court. She said Martha had phoned her and relayed a message from my father. He said to tell me to "stop worrying, that in time everything is going to be all right."

I burst into tears upon hearing his message because I've really been struggling lately. There are days when I feel incredibly lost—like my internal compass has malfunctioned, and I'm grappling to recalibrate it. While I'm trying to move my life in a different direction, as an attorney entrenched in a very busy practice, there's no quick or easy way to do it.

Despite this feeling, though, my awakening continues. I can feel the changes happening inside of me each and every day. Like a lotus flower, I am slowly blossoming and rising up from the mud, although I sense that I still have a fairly long way to go until I fully surface.

A few weeks ago, I read that some people instantly awaken via a "Kundalini awakening." A bolt of lightning, like a trauma, illness, or other powerful event, strikes them internally, releasing Divine energy stored in the base of the spine. This energy then shoots all the way up to the crown chakra, and the person miraculously awakens, becoming one with God while discovering their Divine purpose in the process.

Me, well, I'm obviously on the slow boat to awakening because there's been no fast-acting Kundalini for me.

Speaking of boats, I'm actually on one right now, headed to Harbour Island once again. I arrived at the North Eleuthera Airport twenty minutes ago, immediately hailed a cab to Three Island Dock, and am now on a tender crossing the bay. I've returned to Harbour Island two other times since rescuing Izzie and with this trip, I hope to make major progress in completing my book.

As the tender glides along the water, I stare numbly at the turquoise water of the Bahamas, recalling the events of the past three years. Physically, my life looks so different than it did the day before I rescued Paulie. More importantly, I'm a different person on the inside.

Finally, I'm learning to speak my mind about things that I would have previously kept quiet about. This, however, has put me at odds with several family members and has created tension between me and my mother. She wants me to simply overlook family transgressions and apologize for situations that I didn't create, just to keep the peace; and this is something I am no longer willing to do, especially with—

My thoughts are interrupted, when the tender bumps up against the dock. After the boat captain ties a rope to a piling, I deboard with my bags in hand and look for a familiar face to give me a ride. Not seeing one, I decide to hoof it down the dock and up the steep hill to the inn.

Ten minutes later, winded from hauling fifty pounds of luggage, I arrive at the Bahama House. After settling into my room, I pour myself a glass of

Pinot Grigio from the bottle John has left me as a gesture for my patronage. I walk out onto the gazebo and sit in one of wicker chairs, basking in the serenity of being back at my home away from home.

God, I love this place, I think, taking a sip of my wine.

After a few meditative minutes, I have an "ah-ha" moment, where I connect the dots between my mother's behavior traits and my own. Since as far back as I can remember, I've kept my true feelings hidden, afraid to voice them for fear that family members, friends, and others wouldn't like me. After being bullied for decades, this behavior has become hyper-exaggerated in me, resulting in me suppressing my feelings even more so.

Rarely have I ever heard my mother voice her true feelings because she always keeps her thoughts stoically to herself. A rock with unwavering lack of emotion, a peacemaker who never makes waves, she prefers to remain quietly in the background.

My father, on the other hand, was a basket of emotions. His favorite line was, "I love my kids too much," as we were his everything, his crowning glory, his pride and joy. But a daughter takes more from her mother, I do believe. So like my mother, I've typically kept my feelings to myself.

"You've buried your feelings all this time," I say in a moment of awakening, tears starting to form. "My gosh, that's what made you so ill. It's why you woke up in 2009 feeling like a knife was cutting you across your throat. Your throat chakra was screaming out to be healed: no more burying your feelings, girl!" I slug the remaining wine as a wave of heat rushes through my body.

"I need something to eat," I say, grabbing my tote bag with my laptop in it, along with the key to the golf cart John had graciously reserved for me. And I know just the place to go for a delicious, late lunch—Sip Sip.

Enroute to the restaurant, I stop and pet some of the potcake dogs, who hang out on the island streets. Izzie is actually a potcake, the name given to the mixed-breed dogs (usually brown in color) of the Bahamas. The term potcake comes from the congealed peas and rice mixture that Bahamians traditionally eat, the caked part at the bottom of the pot which is fed to the dogs. Known for being loyal, loving, and incredibly smart, potcakes also have a bit of a stubborn streak about them.

Before I rescued Izzie, I didn't pay much attention to the potcakes living on Harbour Island. Now, every time I visit the island, I find myself looking for familiar potcake faces like Bob, Prince, and many others.

The last time I was on the island, Bob jumped aboard my golf cart, when I was stopped to make a turn and toured around the island with me. At one point, I stopped on Bay Street, so he could take a dip in the water and cool down; and at the end of the day, I rewarded him with a large can of dog food. It was a great couple of hours.

I continue driving toward Sip Sip and arrive a few minutes later. After parking my golf cart down a nearby alley, I head inside the restaurant. "Nikki!" a familiar Bahamian voice exclaims. "You look beautiful! So good to see you again."

Hardly, I think. I've been up since 4:30 a.m., packing and loving on Picasso and Izzie before catching a ride to the airport. I'm still wearing my rumpled clothes that I wore on the plane. "Hi, Carol. It's great to see you as well," I reply. She's one of the servers, who I've known for years.

"Would you like a table?" she asks.

"I'm going to take my favorite seat at the bar, if that's okay?"

"Absolutely! Kathryn will be taking care of you today."

I move to the seat at the far end of the bar next to a wall, providing me with a feeling of being sheltered. That's why I like this place so much. Like the rest of the island, it acts as a respite from the storms raging in my life.

After placing my lunch order, I power on my laptop and open the document for my current *Toads* manuscript. "Let's see where I'm at," I say as I scroll through the document, trying to figure out where I last left off. "Ah, yes, chapter six."

Staring at the screen, my mind wanders to all the people from my past who have spontaneously reappeared in my life the past few years—another symptom of awakening, or so I have read. With almost all of them, there were unresolved feelings that neither of us found closure to. Finally, though, we were able to talk through what had happened and put the past behind us.

Just last week, for example, Gerry, one of my few boyfriends from high school, contacted me, wanting to meet for coffee one afternoon. Ends up, he asked for my forgiveness for standing me up for my senior prom. We laughed about it for twenty minutes, despite the years of hurt it inflicted on my fragile, teenage ego.

There have been other instances where forgiveness has been granted— a few girls who bullied me in school, some former staff members who abruptly left employment, and a couple of cousins have contacted me, all wanting to bury the hatchet. Forgiveness granted. Time to move on. *Se la vie.*

All this forgiveness stuff has been extremely liberating. For years, I've felt like a prisoner trapped by emotions such as bitterness, anger, and resentment. Now, I feel like a huge weight is being slowly lifted from me as I forgive others and, most importantly, forgive myself.

Granted, I still have a long way to go to being completely free of these negative emotions. But slow but sure, I'm making progress as I learn to accept, forgive, and release these situations as a part of my growth and evolution.

Writing the first book of the *Toads* is also helping me gain emotional freedom. With every new chapter I write, I'm releasing another one of the heartaches I've suffered in my journey to find Prince Charming. Besides helping me, my tales will hopefully help others understand that every relationship that comes into our life does so to teach us a valuable life lesson. Damn, those life lessons; they certainly aren't easy to learn.

Kathryn delivers a delicious Pina Colada to me, as I turn my attention back to my manuscript. It's time to get book one of *The Toad Chronicles* series finished and my Divine mission underway. As I begin typing, chapter six about Mannie the "Married Snakus" Toad flows effortlessly into the manuscript.

Chapter Thirty-Eight

Upon my return home, I become increasingly active on social media, meeting people from all over the world while bringing them into my personal realm. It's unsettling at first, sharing my life with complete strangers; but the more I awaken, the more I realize all of us, no matter where we live in the world, are experiencing similar struggles.

Engaging in social media has become a refreshing change to the daily grind of practicing law. Inspiring messages are flowing out of me, and I enjoy posting them, then seeing how people react to them. What I'm really enjoying, though, is all of the posts about animal rescue which flood my daily social media feed.

This week, I happen across a saddening post about two dogs in Turkey which forever changes my life. For some reason, the post strikes a very deep chord in me emotionally, bringing me to tears. I've never reacted so strongly to a photo before, and it's quite upsetting.

Both dogs are suffering immensely: one, a female dog, whose back legs are paralyzed; the other, a large, male Kangal, with a horrific case of rickets. A hulking giant, the dog with rickets had been confined to a shelter for five years which is a very long time in dog years. Thankfully, a woman named "Nadia" stepped in and rescued him, along with the paralyzed female dog.

Even though both dogs are now safe, over the next few days, no matter how hard I try, I can't shake the heartache or erase the image of the dogs from my mind. Wanting to help them, I send a five-hundred-dollar donation to Nadia's organization, hoping to hear back with a "thank you so much for helping." Instead, I hear absolutely nothing—no thank you or acknowledgment, nothing at all.

This doesn't sit well with me, so I message her: "Hi, my name is Nikki Karis. I donated five hundred dollars to your organization, after seeing the post about the paralyzed dog and the one with rickets. I wanted to make certain you received my donation."

Finally, three weeks later, I receive a reply: "Yes, I got your donation. I was stunned by it. It's the largest donation anyone has ever made. Thank you." She offers no further word of why it took so long to reply, how the money will be spent, or any update on the dogs.

"Maybe, she will feed her children with it," I utter in exasperation, clicking out of the message. Being my curious self, though, I continue to follow her social media account to see what develops with the dogs.

A few days later, I'm on my social media account once again, when I see a photo of an adorable, eight-week old puppy, recently rescued from a Turkish junkyard. Jean, who is involved with an animal rescue organization I represent, has shared the post. According to her, a man named "Max" is caring for the puppy, along with several other dogs who are roaming the construction site where he is working. Because Max is planning to return soon to his home in Denmark, he is looking for a Turkish rescue to take the puppy and some of the other dogs.

Staring at the puppy's photo, I think, *How could anyone just discard this precious soul into a junkyard? She has the sweetest, most angelic-looking face. I just don't understand it.*

Something clicks, and I instinctively know that the puppy is meant to be mine. Something clicks again, and I realize that today is November 19th, the same month and day I rescued Paulie back in 2006. Feeling that all of this must be fate, I immediately message Jean, letting her know that I recently donated to a rescue in Turkey and would be happy to try and introduce Max to Nadia.

The next day, Max and I connect via social media. Within our first exchange of messages, I feel like I've found a long-lost brother. A devoted dog lover like me, Max has been on assignment in Turkey for a little over a year and is heartbroken by all the stray dogs he's seen roaming the streets.

According to Max, there are millions of stray dogs living on the streets of Turkey alone. Some dogs with owners aren't treated the best either, often given only scraps to eat, beaten, or tied to a heavy chain for their entire life.

"That's horrible. I had no idea there were so many dogs in need," I message him, my heart crushed thinking about these poor souls.

As Max and I continue messaging each other, I learn that he's been feeding several stray dogs on the site where he works. Two of the dogs, one who he is personally adopting, have already gone to a boarder outside Istanbul, while two other dogs need to get to safety. There are other dogs as well, but they come and go on the site and are not as friendly.

I ask Max to send me photos of the two dogs who he wants to help. When I see their faces, my heart sinks. One of the dogs is brown, tan, and white in color with longer fur and spots on her paws that look like freckles, an Anatolian shepherd mix as Max describes her. She is about seven months old and is suffering from a bad case of mange. I name her Maxine after Max, her angel.

The other dog, who Max has already named Lucky, is a cream-colored Anatolian shepherd and is about five months old. When I see her photo, I do a double-take. Her ears have been cut off, and not by a vet by the looks of things. I message Max: "What in the world happened to Lucky's ears?"

Max explains that livestock guardian dogs like Lucky often have their ears cut off (more like "whacked off"). Owners do this so an animal can't grab hold of the dog while guarding their stock. He detests the practice, as he feels it is an act of animal cruelty, which I agree. Since Lucky is a stray, Max thinks some sick bastard, probably a man, cut her ears off for fun because Turkish men have a horrible reputation for abusing animals.

Tears stream down. *These poor souls have no chance at a future, whatsoever,* I think, surveying the large couch in the recreation room where I'm working from. Immediately, I resolve to adopt Maxine and Lucky as well. I have the room, so why not? These Turkish girls need nourishment, love, and a family to call their own—and I'm happy to oblige. Plus, I need a family to fill my large home.

I message Max: "My decision is made. All three girls are coming to live with me in Florida: Maxine, Lucky, and the junkyard puppy, who I've now named "Mattie," after my mother.

Ecstatic with my decision, I contact Nadia and introduce her to Max via a three-way message. In my message, I explain how I met Max and the fact we have three stray dogs needing a safe place to stay until flying to Florida.

Thankfully, she promptly replies to my message: "Yes, I can help. I will arrange for the dogs' transport to my kennels. Please send four hundred dollars for their transport and initial care. Wire instructions are enclosed." I immediately send her some money, hoping to get the dogs picked up from the site as soon as possible.

The following day, I receive a message from Nadia, verifying that a transport company is scheduled to drive from nearby Bulgaria into Turkey to transport all three dogs to her kennels. The transport is set to take place on Friday which is three days away.

In the days leading up to the transport, I'm super anxious, barely able to sleep or eat, much less focus on my professional responsibilities. Even though I've never met Mattie, Maxine, and Lucky in person, I already love them, dearly. It's like God has brought us all together, to commence upon an unknown journey which will radically change the course of all our lives.

On Friday at 11:00 a.m. Didim time (4:00 a.m. my time), the transport company arrives at the construction site. Max instantly messages me, letting me know that he handed Mattie to the transporters. Lucky was an easy catch, but poor, sweet Maxine got frightened and ran from the construction site. Learning this, I'm devastated thinking she is gone for good.

But the next day, the transport company returns for a second time and successfully captures Maxine. Now, with all three girls safely at Nadia's kennels, I can finally rest easy. My sweet girls should soon be on their way to Florida to live out their remaining days with me.

I turn to Picasso and Izzie and say, "Well, babies, our family will be expanding. Soon, you will have three Turkish sisters to play with. Is this okay with you?"

It's like both of them can understand what I am saying because each one answers me with an affirmative bark. You know, I once read dogs can understand around two hundred words, putting them on par with a two-year old. Amazing, I tell you!

"Okay, then it's a done deal," I say, grabbing their leashes off the countertop in preparation to take them for a walk. "We are now officially known as the 'Karis Animal Sanctuary,' a place where fairy tales do come true."

I clip the leashes onto their collars, and the three of us head out the door, ready for the big adventure awaiting us.

Chapter Thirty-Nine

It's now New Year's Day 2011, and Mattie, Maxine, and Lucky have settled into their temporary life in Turkey. Given Mattie's young age, she is with a foster being doted on, while Maxine and Lucky are being boarded at Nadia's kennels.

I message Nadia and ask when the girls can be flown to Florida. They've been at Nadia's kennels for six seeks now, so they should be ready to travel fairly soon. Replying to my message, Nadia says that she is looking into vaccination requirements for the import of dogs into the U.S. as well as airline options for flying the girls to Florida. She promises to get back with me, as soon as formal arrangements can be made.

Over the ensuing months, I continue donating to Nadia's organization for the care of my Turkish girls along with other dogs she is sheltering at her kennels. During this time, I learn a great deal about the plight of Turkish street dogs, including the thousands upon thousands of dogs living in the forests throughout Turkey.

According to Turkish animal welfare law, street dogs (and cats) are supposed to be vetted by the local municipalities and left to roam freely in their known location. Unfortunately, this rarely gets done, as most municipalities lack a dog catcher. Instead, street dogs are left to survive the harsh elements and are often poisoned, mutilated, raped, and sometimes starved to death, especially when tourist season is at a low.

In the case of the forest dogs, people have illegally dumped them into the forests, where they have little, to no, means of finding food. Thankfully, a couple of times a week, volunteers travel into the forests to feed these poor souls, bringing the elderly, infirmed, and small puppies into safety, space permitting. I donate to one rescue group, hoping to make a small difference.

Some of my social media followers are less than supportive of my philanthropic ventures, though. They feel I should stick with helping American dogs or better yet, humans. I'm even bashed by several people who come onto my page, simply to tear me down.

One crazy woman comments on a photo I post of Maxine: "You idiot piece of shit. There are people starving in this world. And YOU waste your fucking money on dogs."

Wow! She's definitely a bit hostile, so I block her from my account. I certainly don't need any more bullies in my life. Comments like hers only dredge up painful memories from my past, and that's where I intend for her comments like hers to stay—in the past. Besides, it shouldn't matter who I'm helping or where they're from as long as they are being helped.

Then in late February, Max messages me. Back in Turkey, he is working on a new wind propulsion site and has come across a young female puppy, about four months old, living in a nearby village. He relays stories of stopping his car, whistling for her, and seeing her part the bushes, bounding toward him for food and cuddles. Obviously smitten with her, he asks about getting her to Nadia's kennels and then to Florida.

"Of course. There is always room for one more at the Karis Animal Sanctuary. She can stay here, until I find her a forever home," I message him after seeing a photo of her and looking at the massive couch in the recreation room which still has room available on it. She is a beautiful dog with piercing amber eyes, who looks similar to a redbone coonhound although smaller in stature. I can see why Max fell in love with her.

I'm on Harbour Island, at the time, staying at the Bahama House while working on my book. The next afternoon, I take time out from my writing to arrange a call between Max, Nadia, and myself. Max relays the details of the dog's whereabouts which is several hours away from Nadia's kennels. I wire some money to Nadia and before you know it, the young dog is picked up and transported from Canakkale to Nadia's kennels near Didim.

The young dog needs a name. Given her endearing personality and boundless energy, according to Max's accounts, I decide to name her "Joy." I know that whoever ends up adopting this beautiful girl, they will be blessed by all the happiness she brings into their life.

Assisting these poor, helpless creatures is changing something in me. Once tougher than steel from all the heartaches I've endured, my heart is slowly starting to melt. I'm slowly becoming a different person, although I'm not yet certain who that person might be.

My creativity is also in high gear, at this time. The remaining chapters of my book are flowing out of me, and the finish line is in sight. I attribute this to the inspiration my canine kids are channeling my way. Even though I'm separated from my Turkish girls by a huge ocean, I feel their spirit with me every single day, guiding me forward in my journey of awakening.

Then in late April, after another trip to Harbour Island, I finally finish my book. I'm bubbling with excitement to send it off to some literary agents and secure my first publishing deal. Every writer's dream! I spend the next three days writing a query letter and together with the first twenty-five pages of the manuscript, I package it all up and mail copies to three dozen literary agents I've selected from the hundreds of agents I find online.

But I quickly learn that the land of book publishing is a dog-eat-dog sort of world, no pun intended. All of my submissions are rejected—everyone single one of them. Not a single query generates any interest.

One agent actually writes back and says: "Your subject matter is cliché and overdone," adding nothing more.

Welcome to the world of books! I feel totally dejected. My bubble is totally burst; and my plan to escape the nightmare of the pillar is foiled yet again. I realize that I have to return to the more-or-less full-time practice of law, despite having eased out of it somewhat during the final leg and fever-pitch of finishing the book (meaning I'm now working only sixty hours a week versus my standard eighty-plus...sigh).

Then one day, contemplating my painful fate, I realize that the message of my book needs refining. The literary agent is right: the overall theme is cliché and overdone. There are too many books out there about toads (or frogs) magically transforming into Prince Charming. I need a new message that powerfully and uniquely transforms the book into something more. But what can that be?

Powering on my laptop, I stare at the screen, but nothing sparks in me. With no inspiration forthcoming, I check to see if Nadia has messaged me. It's now early June, and I still have yet to hear word as to how and when my girls will be coming to America. I've also agreed to pay for the transport of six other dogs, making a total of ten dogs becoming U.S. dog citizens.

I write to Nadia: "Can you please provide me with a firm date for the transport of my dogs to Florida? This has taken far longer than expected. My dogs need to be with me." Frustrated, I turn off my computer, hoping she will respond in the next couple of days. My heart is heavy. All I want to do is wrap my arms around my girls and start our new life together.

Two days later, she writes back: "I've contacted a transport company to arrange a September travel date. Please send an additional eight hundred dollars for their care."

Yes! Finally, there is a glimmer of hope on the horizon, although it comes with a hefty price tag. I pay it, though—the price, that is—because I want nothing more than to wrap my arms around my precious girls. Since I first laid eyes on their photos last November, I've felt like an anxious parent, waiting to adopt a child from another country. Years often pass by before that parent is finally able to bring their child home to live with them—forever.

Patience, Nikki. Patience. Everything will work itself out in time, I try to assure myself.

Admittedly, I'm losing patience (and faith) in many different areas of my life. I have yet to find my Prince Charming, successfully shift careers, and just be happy. Is that really too much to ask?

Chapter Forty

Now early July, and my faith at another all-time low, I'm busy toiling away at the office, when I decide to take a break and log onto my social media account. Almost immediately, I see a photo of young puppy named "Snuggles" located at an animal shelter in Chipley, Florida come across my feed. Instantly, I know that I must adopt the puppy because I feel a profound calling emanating from the photo, although I'm not exactly certain why I do.

When I tell Clare about my plans to adopt her, though, she's less than supportive. "Nikki, aren't your dogs coming from Turkey soon?" she asks.

"Well, yes, they'll be here in a little over two months, but there's something special about this dog. She's calling my soul."

Clare rolls her eyes and smirks at me. "It's too much, Nikki!" she exclaims. "You really need to give it a rest."

"Never mind. I'm sorry I shared this with you," I respond, realizing a wedge is slowly starting to develop between us which could eventually spell disaster. I shake off any thought of it and return to the mound of legal documents atop my desk.

But Clare isn't the only one who takes issue with me adopting another dog. When I share the news with my mother later that day, she starts to lecture me. She's worried I will never find a husband, having so many dogs.

I say: "Mom I didn't find a husband without dogs. Now, I'm going to follow my heart. If I'm meant to be with someone, he will love me, dogs and all," I say to her. I know she's worried she will die, and I will be left all alone, but I can't allow that to be the reason I forego what's calling from my heart—to adopt Snuggles.

Despite the doubters around me, I fall asleep that night comfortable in my decision to adopt her. I don't care what others think of me. It's my life, and I will adopt as many dogs as I wish.

Then for some unknown reason, in the middle of the night, I sit up straight from a sound sleep and yell, "An adventure ride! That's what I need to do. I need to turn my book into an adventure ride."

I furiously jot my revelation down on the notepad I keep stashed under my pillow and fall back to sleep.

The next morning, I wake, blurry-eyed from a lack of sleep. My thoughts immediately wander to my revelation of earlier in the night. There's no doubt in my mind that Snuggles, who I feel an enormous calling to adopt, caused this epiphany. It's like her very being is breathing new life into my book series.

I look up girl names meaning "life." And bingo! There it is: *Zoie*, the perfect name for my new puppy.

At 9:00 a.m., I call the shelter and speak with the manager. "Hi, this is Nikki Karis. I'm interested in adopting Snuggles. Is she still available?"

"Yes, she is. No one has showed any interest in her," she replies.

"Oh, poor baby! Do you have any background information on her, like how old she is and where she was found?"

"She's about three months old and was found in the woods by herself. A Good Samaritan brought her to the shelter. That's all the information I have on her," she replies.

"Well, her luck just turned. I'm going to spoil her rotten," I say, then give her my credit card information to pay the adoption fee.

We talk for a short while longer about the challenges she faces managing a shelter. As she relays, it's a daily struggle to save as many animals as possible by getting them adopted or out to rescues.

Unfortunately, there simply aren't enough adopters, fosters, or rescues to save them all, and some very adoptable animals end up getting euthanized due to a lack of space. And unethical breeding practices, only exacerbate this problem.

Before I hang up, I promise to assist in whatever way I can. This includes donating toward adoption fees, sending harnesses and collars, and helping with the transport of animals to get them to their respective destinations. It's the least I can do, as these voiceless souls deserve every chance at finding a forever home.

Two days later, I receive a call from a woman named "Andrea," who is assisting with Zoie's transport from the shelter. We arrange to meet at noon in the parking lot of a McDonald's located on Gulf-to-Bay Boulevard in Clearwater. When I arrive, she is standing in the parking lot, holding Zoie in her arms. I park my car and immediately rush over to them, beaming with excitement that Zoie has arrived safely from the shelter.

My heart melts. "Oh, my gosh. She is just the cutest, little thing. Thank you so much for transporting her," I say to Andrea as she hands me Zoie, who has the same familiar shelter stench that Picasso did when I first got him.

"You're welcome. You know, Zoie is the very first dog I've transported who didn't fall asleep in the car. She laid in my lap, wanting to play the whole way," Andrea replies.

"That's my spirited girl," I say.

"Well, I'd love to keep in touch and possibly visit her some time. Do you live nearby?"

"I actually live in Tarpon Springs."

"My sister used to be a teacher at Tarpon Springs High School. Such a small world," she says.

"It's a small world, indeed. I promise to stay in touch and send you updates. Thanks again," I say to Andrea, before we part ways.

When I arrive home, I take Zoie into the recreation room and introduce her to Picasso and Izzie. Zoie is so giddy with excitement that she pees on the couch. No big deal, though; it's an easy, quick clean up.

Thankfully, it's love at first sight for all involved. Izzie, who is now ten months old, immediately takes to mothering Zoie, showing her what's permissible and what's not. Picasso, on the other hand, sits back and watches, like he's keeping a protective eye over the two of them. They are so adorable together—like a bonded, happy family.

Then early that evening, after Zoie has had a bath and settles in with Picasso and Izzie, Andrea texts me letting me know that she's spoken to her sister (the former teacher). She relays that her sister knew my father quite well from when he mentored students at the high school. According to Andrea, my father was incredibly instrumental in her sister's life, helping to inspire her during some difficult and challenging times.

"This is so unbelievable," I text back. "I knew that I was supposed to adopt Zoie but didn't know why until now. Ever since my dad passed on, he has been sending me messages from beyond."

Right then, I know that Zoie and the adventure ride are meant to be. My father has once again appeared in my life, in the most amazing way. "Thank you, Pops, for being my guiding light above," I say, looking toward the heavens.

Anxious to begin revising my book and turning into an inspiring adventure ride, I kiss Picasso, Izzie, and Zoie goodnight. Then I head inside the guest house and power on my laptop, ready to dive into my writing. And I have my new girl, Zoie, to thank for breathing new life into my book and corresponding series.

Chapter Forty-One

For the next two months, I work on revising my book. It's a challenging task because it requires me to switch between present and past tenses, something I've never done before. But since I'm determined to deliver the best book possible, I forge on, writing and rewriting passages sometimes many times over.

During this time period, my law practice is moving full steam ahead. New cases continue to pour in daily, and the mass torts area of my practice is still blossoming. Thus, the only time I have to write is during the middle of the night, after I've managed to shut off the legal side of my brain.

Really, it's more like I live in two brains these days: one representing the lawyer in me; and the other, an aspiring author. But that's okay because I remain hopeful that the day will come when I can become an author and talk show host and leave behind the drudgery of practicing law.

On a good note, Nadia has finally given me a firm date for the transport of Mattie, Maxine, Lucky, and Joy, along with six other dogs that I've agreed to fly to Florida. All of the dogs are females, rescued from the horrors of the streets of Turkey or from some other terrible situation. Four of the dogs have homes, while the other two, Chili and Coco, I plan to adopt out. All ten dogs are set to arrive the third week of September, depending on flight availability.

As planned, a transport company will drive them overnight from Didim to Istanbul, a seven-hour journey, then board them and have them inspected by the government vet. Once the vet clears them for travel, they will board the cargo section of a Lufthansa flight bound for Frankfurt, then layover and be inspected by the German vets.

From there, they will board another Lufthansa flight onto Orlando, Florida. The shipment will take place in two parts: five dogs the first day, then five dogs more two days later.

What an amazing adventure for former street dogs to travel half-way around the world! I am excited beyond measure for them and for myself, as my canine family will be expanding yet again.

To prepare for my new additions, I have wrought iron fencing installed in the back yard, connecting the ends of the breezeway together. This will provide the dogs with a secure area to run, play, and lay around while enjoying the Florida sunshine. I also buy Mattie, Maxine, and Lucky, along with my foster dogs, collars, tags, blankets, toys, and a copious amount of bully sticks. Of course, Picasso, Izzie, and Zoie are showered with these goodies as well. They already have their own stash, but now they have some new things to enjoy.

Perfecto! Everything is set. This has been the longest journey ever—ten months since I saw Mattie's adoring photo. And while I've never met Maxine, Mattie, or Lucky in person, they are now my family, so there is no going back, not ever. No matter how hard dog parenting might be on days, these girls are mine—forever.

Well, the big day finally arrives—September 16, 2011. The dogs are set to depart Nadia's kennels at 11:00 p.m. and travel through the night to Istanbul. Around 4:00 p.m. my time, Nadia calls me via Skype. I answer the call, and she says: "Nikki, there's a problem. We don't have enough travel crates to fit all the dogs. And Coco won't go into her crate. She is really freaked out by it."

"What do you mean, 'You don't have enough crates?'" I snap back. "I bought those crates twice because you claimed the first batch of crates was confiscated by customs."

Nadia then explains that the dogs have grown since they were last measured for their crates (which I find hard to believe). Now, unfortunately, there aren't enough crates to fit all of the dogs. Even if Coco is left behind in Turkey, Nadia is still shy one crate. One of the bigger dogs needs to stay behind, meaning I have to choose between Maxine, Lucky, or Pansy, one of the dogs going to an adopter in Georgia.

I'm tormented, not knowing what to do. Pansy's adopter will be disappointed, if she's left behind in Turkey. As for Maxine, she's been through so much between her mange, getting pregnant at Nadia's kennels, and having her nine babies aborted (an infuriating story for another day). But then there's Lucky—dear, sweet Lucky, who had her ears hacked off by some asshole. Which dog do I choose?

Nadia pressures me. "Nikki, I need an answer now. The transporter is ready to leave."

"Okay, okay, leave Lucky behind. In December, I will fly to Turkey and bring her back as excess luggage," I respond, going purely by instinct, as I've always felt there is something magical about Lucky. She's the strongest of all the dogs and will survive until I can bring her home.

Decision made. The dogs, less Lucky and Coco, depart Didim and arrive in Istanbul early morning the next day.

Two days later, after gaining clearance by the government vet, the first group of dogs departs Istanbul for Frankfurt where they have a ten-hour layover. During the layover, they are taken to a kennel area where they are let out of their crates, fed, given water, and checked by a vet, before being loaded onto their next flight. German people really love dogs, and it shows by the amazing care the dogs receive during their layover.

The following day, I rent a van to transport the dogs from Orlando to Tarpon Springs. A friend of mine, Nancy, goes with me because I will need assistance loading them into the van. We arrive at the Lufthansa cargo area, just as the dogs in their crates are being forklifted into the cargo holding area. I complete some paperwork in the office and wait with Nancy outside the building.

"My girls are finally here. I can't believe it," I turn to her and say with tears streaming down my face, watching the forklift lower the crates onto the floor. "I thought this day would never ever come."

A Lufthansa employee named "Tim" then removes the crates from the pallet and signals me over. "Your dogs are ready, ma'am," he says.

"Oh, my gosh! I've been waiting ten months for this glorious day to arrive. All of them were rescued off the streets of Turkey."

"It's a wonderful thing you've done, ma'am. These dogs are very blessed to have you."

"Aww, that's sweet of you, but I'm the one who is blessed," I say, bending down to peer inside the crates. I want to hug my babies so bad, but I'm afraid to let them out. Rescue dogs, street dogs especially, are infamous for backing out of their collars and taking off running, until they are firmly settled into their new surroundings. I've read stories about dogs having taken off at airport cargo, never to be found.

Before loading them into the rental van, I pour some water into the plastic containers secured to their crate doors to help quench their thirst. Together, Nancy, Tim, and I load them into the back of the van and secure their crates using tie down straps.

"Thank you so much, Tim. I really appreciate your help," I say, handing him some money as a tip. "We will be back in two days for the arrival of the second shipment."

"You have a safe drive, ma'am," he says, closing the back door to the van.

The girls sleep soundly on our way home. There's not a peep out of them, although there's a strong stench emanating from the back of the van that's enough to make me gag. Thankful for a night of low humidity, Nancy and I drive home with the windows down.

When we arrive at my house, we unload the crates inside the courtyard. Once the gate is securely locked (I double-check it, just to be sure), we open the crate doors and let the girls take their first steps on American soil. Mattie is the first one out of her crate followed by sweet, shy Maxine. Bonnie and Cameo, both going to adopters in other states, make their way out of their crates next.

They look a bit shell-shocked, like they don't know what to make of their new surroundings. So I sit down in the grass and talk sweetly to them, assuring them that everything is all right: "It's okay, babies. You're home. You're finally home."

Tears stream down my face, thinking of how blessed these girls are to be here in this very moment. Sadly, there are hundreds of millions of street dogs around the world who will meet a far different fate. I so wish I could save them all, but I am doing what I can for now.

While the girls continue sniffing around the courtyard, I head inside the recreation room and prepare four small bowls of food. I don't want them eating too much for their first American meal, as they've traveled a very long distance over the past four days.

Before feeding them, I separate them into different areas of the courtyard because Nadia warned me that streets dogs can be food aggressive given their tough start to life. I don't want them fighting and getting injured, not after all they've been through to get here.

Meanwhile, Nancy finishes washing out their crates, then she puts them inside the recreation room with a fresh blanket inside each one. When the girls are done eating, I bring them inside the recreation room and allow them to explore for a while. The girls then bunk down for the night, wary from their long travels. I sleep on the couch to keep a watchful eye over them, while Picasso, Izzie, and Zoie sleep in the guest house.

Nancy and I repeat the same steps two days later, until all eight dogs are at my home, safely inside the enclosure of my courtyard. Finally, my girls are home where they belong, although my heart is breaking for Lucky, who is left behind in Turkey.

"Baby girl, I promise that I won't leave you behind. You'll be with all of us by Christmas," I say, looking up to the heavens, hoping God will hear me and answer my prayers. I then head inside the guest house to work on my book.

Powering on my laptop, I think: *There is something so incredibly special about Lucky that I just can't put my finger on. She represents the completion of a journey that I've been on which began March of 1999, when I made my first trip to Harbour Island in the Bahamas.* I have no idea exactly what this means, so I dismiss any further thoughts about it and dive into my writing.

Chapter Forty-Two

One of the most joyous times in life for me has been acquiring a new dog. I don't know if all dog owners feel the same way, but that's been my experience so far. But I haven't just acquired one new dog; I now have a gaggle of them. In one fell swoop, I've gone from having three dogs to five dogs while fostering six others.

And while the arrival of my Turkish girls has been exponentially joyous, it's also come with its fair share of challenges. Zoie, the youngest of the pack at five months old, isn't yet fully adjusted to her environment. Now, I have two more dogs to fit into my daily routine, along with keeping six fosters happy and healthy until they move onto their forever homes.

Phew! I pray I'm up for the task because it seems a bit overwhelming right now.

To help acclimate the Turkish girls, I'm working from home for the next two weeks with Adam assisting me. Today is bath day, so we round up the girls and take them onto the dog run behind the recreation room. After bathing them (no easy task, mind you, as this appears to be their very first bath—ever), we leave them on the run to dry off.

When I look out onto the run a while later, I see them laying close together, lapping up the sunshine. Just like sisters should be—bonded together, forever, through thick and thin. My heart breaks, thinking of the strained relationship with my own sister, wishing it were different.

A few days later, once the weariness of their journey wears off, the girls' true personalities start to emerge. Each one's personality is so unique, as are their specific needs and wants. I never knew dogs had such huge personalities; at least not until I rescued Paulie that fateful November day.

Four of the fosters, Cameo, Pansy, Spice, and Bonnie, will be leaving for their forever homes over the coming days. That will leave Joy and Chili, who Nadia asked me to ship to Florida, to find homes for. Upon arriving at my home, I changed Chili's name to "Zaida," meaning fortunate one, because it's a far more fitting name for a royal-looking canine like her.

Right now, the girls are acting like kids in a candy shop. Everything is so new and exciting to them. They love to explore outside, roll around in the grass, lounge on the massive couch in the recreation room, and chew on bully sticks.

Pansy, a mix of Great Pyrenese and Anatolian Shepherd, dog breeds traditionally used for herding, has also found her favorite perch—on top of the granite countertops. She apparently likes to be up high, looking down upon the other dogs. And when she's behind me, she likes to push her nose into my rear end as though herding me around like I'm a goat. I guess you can take a herding dog out of the fields, but you can't take the herding instinct out of the dog.

But it's not all roses and doggies, mind you. The girls are acting like they're living back on the street, digging huge craters in the courtyard, peeing in the recreation room, and performing other naughty feats. I've now sopped up my sixth puddle of pee this morning, and the girls have only been awake for two hours. They definitely need some training, at least in the potty department.

And Mattie, well, she arrived in Florida looking like a Sudanese refugee. I did a double-take, when she first emerged from her crate, because she was alarmingly thin with her hip bones protruding out.

When Mattie was fostered in Turkey, she was well-nourished, according to the photos I received of her. But when Mattie arrived at Nadia's kennels four or five months before departing for Florida, she seemed to go downhill. You know, I really need to speak with Nadia and found out exactly what happened to her.

Later that night, I Skype with Nadia and attempt to address my concerns about Mattie and the other girls. In response, Nadia becomes extremely defensive, blaming me for the girls' misbehavior. She also denies any ill-care of Mattie, claiming she lost weight while in Istanbul waiting to board the flight to Frankfurt.

"That much weight loss in such a brief time?" I ask.

"You obviously don't know dogs. You are an amateur," she retorts.

Instead of pushing the issue, I decide to just let it rest for the time being. She has Lucky, and the last thing I want to do is piss her off and risk never getting Lucky home. I disconnect the call, feeling ever more frustrated.

As for Picasso, I'm still hesitant about introducing him to the Turkish girls. He tends to be protective of me and also jealous around new dogs. I know he feels left out, living in the guest house, but I want to give the girls more time to settle in before making an introduction.

And Izzie and Zoie, well, you would never know they aren't Turkish. They're now part of the new girls' pack, or maybe it's the other way around. Who really knows? All I know is the world would be a much better place if humans got along as splendidly as my Turkish, Bahamian, and American born girls are getting along right now.

Zoie, the youngest and smallest dog of the pack, seems to be taking the lead and showing everyone the ropes. She's become the resident greeter of the estate, kissing each of the girls when they enter back into the recreation room after being outside. Earlier this afternoon, when I checked in on them, I found she and Mattie spooning with each other, while napping on the treadmill. So cute, I tell you!

I look at my watch. It's 9:00 a.m., time to feed the dogs. I say to Adam, "Can you get their food ready?" Then suddenly, I hear a commotion coming from the courtyard. The dogs are barking uncontrollably, but I have no idea what has caused such a stir. I quickly corral them inside to avoid upsetting the neighbors, but one dog is missing—Pansy.

Fearing she's somehow escaped outside the fencing, I run back outside, but she's nowhere to be found. I panic. "Adam, come quick. Pansy is gone," I yell to him. Adam drops the dogs' stainless steel foods bowls into the sink creating a loud thud and runs outside.

Then I hear a horn honking from the front of the house. It clicks. "Pansy's been hit!" I exclaim as Adam and I take off running.

Out front of my house, there's a street with a bayou of water located on the other side. The bayou is a beautiful view to behold; although right now, all I fear viewing is Pansy lying dead in the middle of the road. Thankfully, there's no body. Instead, a man, who has pulled his car onto the easement, yells: "Miss, your dog is on the roof."

"What?" I yell back, then turn around to see Pansy perched on a section of flat roof located on the second story. *That's what the other dogs were barking at*, I think before saying to the man, "Thank you so much." He waves and drives off.

Pansy was rescued by Nadia off the street in Didim, after Nadia witnessed a group of young girls throwing rocks at her. Yes, even children abuse animals which is a sad testament to the current state of Humanity. Pansy and Spice are going to an adopter in southern Georgia; that's if I can safely get her down off the roof.

"Adam, grab some pillows and blankets and drop them by the roof line at the side of the guest house. That will cushion Pansy, if she falls. And call the fire department to see if they can come and help."

After he runs off, I begin talking to Pansy, trying to coax her from the front of the house toward the side near the guest house. There's a large concrete stairway located between the buildings of the recreation room and guest house which she must have scaled to get onto a section of the flat roof then onto the second story tiled one.

As Pansy makes her way around the tiled roofline, she begins to slip because there's still morning dew on the tiles. Thankfully, she catches herself but remains in a state of suspended animation. "Oh, my gosh! Oh, my gosh! Adam, get the ladder. Quick!"

Promptly returning with the ladder, Adam sets it up in the narrow passageway between the main house and guest house. I quickly scale it, hoping to avert a doggie disaster. Given the angle of this area of roof and the large gutter abutting it, though, I'm unable to reach Pansy.

"Grab the bathroom rugs inside the guest house. I need something with traction to throw onto the roof," I yell to Adam while standing on the top rung of the ladder. I look down and pray that I don't fall onto the walkway, as it will definitely hurt like hell, if I do.

"Hold on, baby girl. Hold on. I'm going to get you down," I say to Pansy worried that a fall from the roof will result in her demise and maim me in the process.

Adam comes back with the rugs, climbs up the ladder, and hands them to me. Right then, I hear a commotion at the back of the house. "It must be the fire department. Please go and let them inside the gate," I say to Adam.

I return to the task of throwing the rubber-backed rugs onto the tile roof to give Pansy something with traction to walk on. Thankfully, my efforts are successful, as Pansy makes her way onto the rugs and off the steep angled roofline then onto a portion of the flat roof. The firemen, who have now scaled the cement staircase onto the flat roofline, pick her up in their arms and return her to ground zero.

"Phew! That was enough excitement for one morning," I say to one of the firemen, who I've known for many years. "I wasn't certain you even took these kinds of calls. You hear about this kind of stuff in the movies, but I didn't know if it applied in real life."

"You'd be surprised by some of the calls we get. Last week, we rescued a kitten out of a storm drain. We do our best to help out when we can," he says, waiting for the other two firemen to finish taking photos with Pansy, who is lapping up all the attention she is getting.

I shake my head and think, *She is too much! She definitely keeps me on my toes. I really wish she wasn't going to an adopter because I'd love for her to stay here with me.*

Once the firemen leave, Adam resumes with feeding the girls. Meanwhile, I head into the guest house to feed Picasso and fix something to eat for myself. While I'm waiting for my eggs to boil, I power on my laptop and email Nadia. "Can you please advise of a date when I can come to Turkey to retrieve Lucky? I really want to get her home where she belongs," I write, heartsick she isn't already with me.

I return to making breakfast, hoping to hear some news from Nadia in the coming days. She is really starting to annoy me, but I have to keep my cool. My precious Lucky is in her possession.

Chapter Forty-Three

Well, the day has finally arrived when Bonnie, Spice, and Pansy leave for their forever homes in Georgia. I'm driving them to the Florida Welcome Center located at the Florida-Georgia border on I-75. Their respective adopters, both residing near the Atlanta area, are set to meet me at noon.

Cameo, on the other hand, is flying out tomorrow morning from Tampa International Airport. She will fly to Atlanta, have a two-hour layover, then fly onto Omaha, Nebraska. Her adopter will pick her up from the cargo department for U.S. Airways.

I'm totally crushed. During the past two weeks, I've grown so attached to the girls. I will miss them all so much.

Tears stream down as Adam and I begin to load the girls into their travel crates, which he put into the Rover the night before. I kiss each girl, rub them all over, and assure them that they are welcome back with me should anything go wrong in their new home.

"I love you. Thank you for being a part of my journey," I whisper softly to each one before locking their crate door.

The trip to the Florida-Georgia border will take about four hours which will give me plenty of time to think. Driving, my thoughts wander to the past five years since my father passed away.

What a tumultuous ride it has been...intense grief, family struggles and strife, financial devastation, professional challenges, a still ongoing construction nightmare at my home, a pretty much non-existent dating and sex life, a health crisis followed by a period of intense detox, and much,

much more, all wrapped up in a big, fat package described by Lily as an "awakening."

"Yeah, I got your awakening, Lily. It's more like undergoing an enema with a stick of dynamite," I chuckle, thinking of the sheer volume of shit that I've expelled from my life since February of 2007.

According to Lily, the world, in another ten years or so, will undergo a massive awakening—millions upon millions of people, all expelling their shit at the same time. "Be thankful you're going through the process now," Lily said during our last lunch. "When the planetary awakening hits, it won't be pretty. But for you, you'll understand what's going on. You'll be able to help others through the process."

Okay, let's get moving. I'm ready, willing, and able to assist, I think, passing a car in front of me that's moving at a snail's pace.

Then I remember a passage from *Zorba the Greek* by Nikos Kazantzakis. An ex-boyfriend gave me a copy of the book, before I ever started down my path of awakening, and shortly after I gifted him a copy of *Hope for the Flowers*. The passage is really quite profound.

Alexis Zorba, the main character, comes upon a cocoon hanging in a pine tree, just as the husk is breaking open and the inner soul is preparing to emerge. Waiting, and becoming impatient that the process is taking too long, he breathes onto the cocoon to warm it and speed the process along. The husk breaks and the butterfly emerges, but its wings are sadly crumpled. It cannot fly as much as it tries.

Zorba attempts in vain to assist the butterfly by breathing on it, but it's too late. The butterfly dies. Nature's everlasting rhythm is violated because Zorba is impatient. *Patience*—that word. Oh, how I loathe it.

I feel like I've been more than patient while stuck in my cocoon, waiting to become like Yellow. I'm forty-four years old and still have yet to experience anything even remotely akin to a normal life. Nothing. Nada. Not a shred of normalcy about my life.

Maybe I just need more time, more finetuning and polishing, before I break the husk and emerge as Yellow, and Stripe miraculously appears in my life. I don't know. It's all so exhausting. I wish I could just tune it all out. I really, really do.

Pansy stirs in her crate, letting out a soft bark as though she's read my thoughts telepathically and sympathizes with me. What an amazing soul of a dog she is. All dogs are, really. Given the right opportunity, their souls literally spring to life, and shine like a diamond. And that's what I want to do. I want to emerge from my cocoon, and shine.

Focusing on my driving, I tune out any further thoughts about the current state of my life because it tends to make me anxious. Besides, I have more important things to focus on: like getting my precious cargo to their adopters.

A short while later, I arrive at the Florida Welcome Center. The adopters are already there, awaiting my arrival. After a brief introduction, I give the adopters a summation of the girls' progress, likes, dislikes, eating and sleeping habits. Together, we then transfer the girls' travel crates from the Rover into their respective vehicles.

Before departing, and while holding back tears, I say to both adopters, "If for any reason things don't work out, please know the girls are always welcome back with me." We wave goodbye to each other. And like that, three pieces of my heart are gone—forever.

Huge, crocodile tears pour forth for much of the drive back home. Already, I miss Bonnie, Spice, and Pansy, as they brought so much happiness and joy into my life. And to think; I have to go through this same heartache tomorrow with Cameo, then with Joy and Zaida when they head to their forever homes.

"Well, that's it! Joy and Zaida are staying with me," I say, slamming my hand down onto the steering wheel. "I've been through so much getting them to Florida and have spent a boatload of money doing it. There's plenty of room for them and dozens of other dogs, if I so choose. Screw that dream of a normal life. It will be me and my Goddogs from now on."

Decision made. Joy and Zaida are now a part of the Karis Animal Sanctuary. Forget about a husband and kids, at least for the time being. Now, to get Lucky to Florida, and my family will be complete.

I arrive home a few hours later, exhausted from the long drive. Instantly, I'm greeted with tons of doggie kisses from the girls. Cameo, though, stays to herself in one corner of the recreation room, as she is shyer and more reserved than her Turkish sisters.

It's an exhilarating feeling to be so loved. Only one person in my life loves me unconditionally like these dogs do, and that's my dear, sweet mother. I'm so grateful she is still with me. Even though we've had some heated moments the past few years, I don't know what I would do without her love and support.

"Adam, I'm going into the guest house to spend time with Picasso and catch up on my emails. Do you need help with anything?" I ask.

"No, thanks. I've got things covered," he replies.

"Well, I better break the news to you now versus later, but I've decided to keep Joy and Zaida."

Chuckling, he says, "Like I didn't already know that." He returns to washing the bowls, while the girls lay on the tile floor and watch him intensely. They love him so much, and he loves them. It's comforting to know someone so caring looks after them when I'm at work or away.

Once inside the guest house, I rub on Picasso for a while, then open the door and let him out into the courtyard. Unbeknownst to me, though, Adam has already let the girls outside. Panic sets in.

"Adam!" I scream, worried a fight is about to ensue. He immediately runs outside. But instead of a fight ensuing, Picasso starts sniffing each girl's butt. This, as I've come to learn, is the way dogs meet and greet each other—the way they size each other up.

Thankfully, everyone's tails are wagging, and the meet and greet is an enormous success. A few minutes later, all of the dogs are running around the courtyard, playing and having fun. Adam stays outside to watch them, while I head back inside the guest house, my heart welling up from the joy of the moment.

I power on my laptop, hoping to have received a message from Nadia, but there is nothing from her. Frustrated, I start to message her again, then decide to give her more time to respond. Surely, she isn't going to keep Lucky. That would be so very wrong.

Chapter Forty-Four

Since arriving in Florida six weeks ago, my Turkish girls, or "Turkish princesses" as I now call them, are slowly, but surely, settling into a daily routine. Adam, who has now been working for me a little over two years, is so kind and patient with them, helping them acclimate to life as domesticated, spoiled pooches.

Meanwhile, I'm back in my office dealing with Billy Boy and similar stiffs who occupy the defense side of personal injury law. I'm also back to writing my inspirational messages and sharing them online. The progress on my book, though, has come to a screeching halt.

Writer's block! I've heard it can last days, weeks, even months on end. No doubt, it has something to do with Lucky to whom I'm spiritually tied. My creativity is at an all-time low, as my mind has been focused elsewhere—on getting her home to where she belongs.

As for my Turkish princesses living in Florida, each one is blossoming and developing the most unique personality, while happiness and unconditional love exude from their every pore. It's amazing to watch them transform from being once outcasts living on the streets of Turkey to thriving, loving homebodies.

First, there is Mattie, who started me down the path of adopting Turkish street dogs. She gets her name from my mother, Ruth, whose given first name is actually Mattie. I chose that name, meaning "strength in battle," because *strength* is what I need as the battle within my immediate family ensues.

When she first arrived, Mattie was suffering from severe separation anxiety. She also looked like a refugee, who had made a long, weary trip without food or water. On top of that, she exhibited up to seven different personalities, depending on her mood. At one point, I thought she might have descended from a Buddhist Monk. As nutty as it sounds, she would hum like a monk in meditation mode: "Hmm, hmm, hmm"—a nervous reaction, no doubt, caused by her anxiety.

And then there were her sudden explosions into mania, like Sybil might do. She would tear pillows and blankets into the smallest of shreds. There's no question she was traumatized by the separation from her mother at a very young age and then later from her foster parent. It haunts her, even to this day. But slowly, she is settling in and realizing this is her home, where she will be safe from the perils of the outside world. And while her bouts of mania still ensue, they are becoming less frequent.

Princess Mattie Puss Puss—that's what I adoringly call her. She loves to lay on the back of the couch like a cat, unperturbed by everything around her. And she has quite a prima donna attitude about her, preferring to pee on the towel I leave on the floor because it's apparently beneath her to pee outside in the courtyard like the rest of the dogs.

Which is not to say she dislikes other dogs. In fact, she loves her big brother Picasso—a lot. She follows him around, lays and sleeps next to him, and shows affection toward him in the most endearing ways. Izzie has since bonded with Zoie, Maxine, Zaida, and Joy (the "Girls' Club"), so Picasso now has a new little sister, all to himself.

But Mattie saves most of her love for me. At night, she sleeps with me, along with Picasso and Izzie, and will snuggle up as close as she can to me. It's as though she's been appointed my personal "watcher" by God Himself, sent with the sole purpose of holding unconditional love for me.

Maxine, on the other hand, still has a bit of wild hair in her. She's the dog who initially ran from the transporters, only to be captured the next day. I still thank God for those amazing transporters because, without them, Maxine would be another sad street dog statistic.

Upon arriving at my home, she was incredibly shy. For the first three weeks, I wasn't able to get within five feet of her. I'd approach her, and she would back away. It's the same way feral animals act, instincts tuned to survival and the notion that anything coming at them could be injurious.

Slowly, she is overcoming her fears and becoming more relaxed. The other day, she actually let me pet her full on—a small miracle. That precious moment, albeit brief, put a huge smile on my face because I want nothing more than for her (and the rest of my pack) to feel loved and safe.

Maxine's name means "greatest, bright, noble" and is genuinely befitting of her. She is the quintessential "poster-dog" for making a complete transformation from a once mangy-looking creature into a dog of sheer beauty. Every single day, she brings brightness into my life, just by her very presence.

With her piercing, amber-colored eyes, Joy was twice the age of Mattie when she was rescued in February of 2011. Compared to Mattie and Maxine, she arrived in Florida possessing an incredible amount of confidence. She not only welcomes human interaction, but she actually thrives on it. Highly intelligent, quick on her paws, witty in her actions, and just an all-around great dog, all of these things describe Joy to perfection.

That said, she does have one odd behavior trait. Strange as this may sound, she has a thing for my breasts. Seriously—I'm not kidding. I know it sounds a bit strange, but it's the God's honest truth.

Whenever I sit next to her, she immediately (I mean, within like two seconds) shoves her head up my shirt and plants it firmly between my breasts. There's no chance for escape. She's that fast!

Thankfully, she doesn't try to nurse, as that would totally freak me out and put a huge damper on her party. She just lays there, totally content, until I manage to peel her off of me.

I don't know if my heartbeat makes her feel secure; or if she missed bonding with her mother, but this is what I deal with every single day. So now, I'm teaching her about "personal space" because I want her to understand that unsolicited behavior like hers is not okay.

Zaida, with her golden eyes and shiny black coat, is different than her Turkish sisters in an upsetting way. Unlike her sisters, she wasn't rescued off the street; rather, Nadia pulled out her of a home where she was being raised to eventually dog fight. Thankfully, Nadia got her out in time because it doesn't appear that any psychological damage was done.

Dog fighting! The thought of it makes my blood boil. It's hard for me to imagine why anyone would subject an animal to such a cruel and barbaric sport. So much violence, so many animals dead, all due to the selfish nature of certain sub-humans.

Yes, I call them "sub-humans." They don't deserve the title of *humans* because that word is associated with the word *humane* which means to be compassionate. And that, they are definitely not.

Anyway, I'm so grateful Zaida is part of my heart and home because she is the absolute sweetest soul. She's quite comical, too. Whenever we converse together, she makes the funniest faces, eyes wide open and lips contorted, coupled with her goofy sounds. Her favorite activity, though, is rolling over for belly rubs. That's a sure sign of a dog's trust—a dog who is definitely a lover and not a fighter.

And then there's dear, sweet Lucky: my girl without ears, who is six thousand miles away. Not a day goes by that I don't think about her or feel her spirit with me.

I close my eyes and picture her at Nadia's kennels, protected from the dangers of the outside world, yet yearning to be home with me and her siblings. Tears stream down my face as I say a prayer to God, asking Him to protect her and keep her safe, until I can make the long journey to Turkey to bring her home with me.

Chapter Forty-Five

One week later, I make a fatal error that ends up costing me Lucky or rather, it costs Lucky her freedom and a ticket home to Florida.

The tension with Nadia had been building for months, so I should have seen it coming. Actually, I should have seen the entire situation more clearly from the first donation I made which she failed to acknowledge, but hindsight is always 20/20. Besides, without her assistance, I wouldn't have Mattie, Maxine, Joy, and Zaida, so not all is a loss.

However, on Thursday afternoon when I'm at my office, I post photos of my Turkish princesses on my social media account. In response, a friend comments, questioning why Mattie looks so thin. She is worried I'm not feeding her enough.

Without thinking, I comment back that Mattie's weight loss started when she was at Nadia's kennels in Turkey. I explain that I am doing my best to fatten her up, although it is taking time. The post is public, so anyone can see it along with all of the comments.

Well, less than ten seconds later, Nadia messages me; and she is more than a little irate. "How dare you speak ill of me! I will not tolerate it. All of this is your fault, all of it. I should have never given *my* dogs to you."

"*Your* dogs? Mattie, Maxine, Lucky, and Joy are *my* dogs. Max rescued them, gave them to me, then together he and I contacted you about caring for them until they could fly to Florida. They were never *your* dogs."

By this time, I am frantic, so I type: "Now, I want a firm a date in December when I can come to Turkey and bring Lucky home."

"I will never give you Lucky—never," she writes back. "She is mine, and I will decide what happens to her, not you."

"You can't just keep my dog. I paid for her rescue from the construction site, transport to your kennels, care while she was with you, vetting expenses, and her travel crate twice," I type, then decide to add more, "besides that, I supported your rescue for months, along with donated a generous sum of money for the start of your new kennels which, let me remind you, are named in honor of my father. Understand that I will take legal action against you to get her back." I try to send my message, but Nadia has already blocked me.

Right then, Clare walks into my office. "Is anything wrong, Nikki? You look upset."

"I can't believe it. Nadia blocked me. She is refusing to give me Lucky."

"That's awful. I know you were looking forward to Lucky joining your pack. Please don't let it get you down," Clare says.

"Well, I can't just let it go. I can't let Lucky live out the rest of her days in the hell of a Turkish kennel. She represents the completion of a journey I've been on. I have to see this through to the end."

"Look, I hate to see you so upset. I'm sure you will find another dog to fill the void. She is *just* a dog, after all."

"*Just* a dog? Lucky is a soul with a purpose, and that purpose is to be with me and the rest of my pack. If I have to fly to Turkey and snatch her from those godforsaken kennels myself, that's what I will do. I will never give up getting my girl home where she belongs," I say, gathering some things off my desk and throwing them in my briefcase. "Please run cover for me, okay? I need to get out of here."

"Sure thing. I'll see you in the morning," Clare says as I head out the door to my office down the hallway toward the lobby.

Before opening the door, I stop because I want to say something more to Clare. Her comment about Lucky being *just* a dog is really upsetting me.

But I decide to shrug it off, as the last thing I need is conflict with Clare. I have way too much on my plate these days as it is.

Once inside the Rover, I start bawling. I don't know why I'm reacting this way because I've never even seen Lucky in person, much less wrapped my arms around her. But I feel an incredibly strong, spiritual connection to her that is hard to describe. The phrase "she represents the completion of a journey" keeps replaying in my head.

"What does that mean?" I ask myself, trying to figure out an obvious message sent to me by the Universe since it has come to me more than once. "The only journey I'm on right now is one of awakening and becoming Yellow, but I don't understand how Lucky ties into all of that. It just doesn't make sense."

For a short while, I sit in the Rover trying to decipher the message, then decide to call it quits. I start the engine and head for home, stopping by mother's house on the way. She took the day off from the office, so she has no idea what has transpired with Lucky.

"Oh, honey, I'm so sorry," she says, after I relay my conversation with Nadia. "I know how much Lucky means to you."

"I'm totally heartbroken over it," I say, tears forming in my eyes.

"Well, your father used to have a saying that he lived by, 'Nothing is impossible.' No matter how badly the deck was stacked against him, he always found a way. Now, don't you give up on Lucky. You'll figure a way to get her. You hear me?"

"I will never give up," I reply. "Failure isn't coded into our bloodlines."

"You're a fighter, just like your father used to be. He loved you so much. In you, he saw all the things he regretted not doing in his own life, like going to college and law school."

"I miss him more than anything in this world. And I know you miss him, too," I say.

"I sure do, honey. He was the love of my life."

"Tell ya what. Let's you and I go for an early dinner. Give me thirty minutes to run home and change," I say, grabbing my keys off the table, readying to leave.

"I'd love that. And honey, I've been meaning to apologize to you for what I said before. You know, when I told you that you'd never find a husband having all those dogs. Don't you listen to an old woman like me. You do what's right for you."

"Thanks, but you're hardly an old woman. You're the most inspiring person I know," I say, reaching over and kissing her on the cheek. "Now, let me run so I can get back here. I love you."

On my way home, I reminisce about the incredible trips my mother and I have taken together through the years: backpacking through Europe after I attended college in London for a semester; a safari in Kenya, including a hot air balloon ride over the Serengeti, for my thirtieth birthday; cruising the Galapagos Islands not too long after my father died; several visits to Harbour Island through the years, and many more amazing trips.

And to think. She was raised on a small farm in north Florida with little chance of upward socio-economic mobility. Yet, she took a chance and left the family farm in search of opportunity.

While working as a relief telegraph operator, she met my father. Three months later, they got married and raised a beautiful family, including three children—me; my brother, who is nineteen years older than me; and my sister, who is fourteen years older. In between, they managed to see a large part of the world.

At eighty-seven years old, she is my greatest inspiration, serving as a constant reminder that anything in life possible, no matter a person's age. She has never stopped evolving and growing, even to this day.

With that inspiring thought filling my heart, I pull into the portico of my home, turn off the engine to the Rover, and vow to make this next chapter of my life my best one yet.

Chapter Forty-Six

Two days later, on Wednesday afternoon, I receive an unexpected call from Pansy's adopter. "Hi, Nikki, this is Darla, Pansy's mom."

"Oh, hi, Darla. Nice to hear from you. Is everything all right?"

"Well, the reason for my call..."

Darla then proceeds to tell me that Pansy hasn't been able to train to the invisible fence she had installed at her home, something that had concerned me when I first heard about it. Pansy slipped through the fence again last week and almost got hit by a car.

"Thank goodness she's okay," I say.

"I know, I know," Darla replies. "Look, I hate to do this because I've grown attached to Pansy, but I think it would be better if I gave her back to you. Is there any chance you could pick her up on Friday?"

I glance at my calendar. Thankfully, all I have are some phone conferences that can be moved. I ask her, "Can we meet at noon at the Florida Welcome Center?"

"Sure. That's perfect," Darla replies. "Pansy and I will see you then."

I hang up the phone, elated that Pansy will be returning. She has the most amazing spirit, although I could do without her walking across the granite countertops and scaling the roof. It's a small price to pay, though, for the opportunity to be her forever mom.

Friday arrives, and I make the four-hour journey to the Florida Welcome Center, where I find Darla waiting for me. She has Pansy on a leash and is walking her around in a grassy area. When Pansy sees me, she bolts out of Darla's arms and runs full-steam towards me. I immediately grab onto her leash, as she bearhugs me around my legs.

"Phew! That was a close call," I exclaim to Darla, relieved that Pansy didn't take off running in the opposite direction.

"She is one strong and stubborn dog with a mind of her own," Darla says.

"I know this must be hard on you," I say. "But rest assured, Pansy will be well taken care of and very much loved."

"Oh, I know she will be. When I told Nadia I was giving Pansy back to you, she was really upset. I told her it was my decision, not hers."

"Upset? Why would she be upset? I paid for all of Pansy's expenses to fly to Florida. Gawd, that woman infuriates me."

Right then, Pansy starts tugging on the leash. "Well, it looks like she is ready to go. Are you sure about this?" I ask Darla, wanting to give her one last chance to change her mind.

"Yes, yes, now go on. Get out of here," she says, before reaching down and giving Pansy several pats on the head. She then heads for her car.

"Safe travels, Darla. I'll keep you updated on Pansy's progress."

With her back turned, she gives me a quick wave. My heart breaks for her, watching her get into her car, as I sense that she is crying.

After Darla pulls away, I walk Pansy toward the Rover. "Come on, baby girl. Let's get on the road," I say as she jumps into the back seat that is covered with sherpa blankets, fitting for a dog of her breed. I hook her leash into one of the seatbelts to prevent her from climbing into the front seat while I'm driving. The two of us then take off for home.

"Baby girl, guess what? I've decided to change your name to Tanzi," I say to her about half an hour into our drive. "What do you think? Do you like your new name?"

Tanzi lets out several barks, and I think back to the previous night when a friend commented on Tanzi's photo that I had posted on my social media account. The friend said there was something very *spiritual* about her, like she had lived many lifetimes before this one. For whatever reason, the comment made me think of my favorite stone, Tanzanite, considered to be a highly spiritual stone. From there, the name "Tanzi" was born.

Three hours later, Tanzi and I pull into the portico at my house. "You're home, baby girl," I say to her, unclipping her leash from the backseat and escorting her inside the courtyard. And what a party it turns out to be!

All of the dogs, Picasso included, immediately run out into the courtyard to greet their beautiful, blonde sister. There's a ton of butt-sniffing going on, some jostling back and forth, a lot of happy barks, even a couple of tandem dive bombs into the grass. But it's obvious from their actions that everyone is happy to have Tanzi back home.

Chapter Forty-Seven

Craving some of her sage advice, I call Lily a few days later and invite her to lunch. Lately, despite all the positive things happening on the canine-front, I've been feeling increasingly frustrated that my awakening is taking so long. I want to check in with her to see what, if anything, she recommends I do to move things along without compromising the process.

"You're pushing too hard, Nikki," she says, after I explain that I'm feeling trapped in my cocoon with no escape in sight. "With what you've been through these past five years, most people would have cracked. You need to slow down and allow yourself time to heal, before moving onto the next phase."

"But I want to get a new chapter of my life underway."

"I know you do, but you can't rush God. He has a very specific strategy mapped out for your awakening, transformation, and ultimate rise into your Divine destiny. You will fly like a butterfly when He deems it's the right time."

I sigh heavily, and Lily continues, "Look, Nikki, you're one of the most powerful, spiritual beings I know, as you're incredibly connected to God. But with that connection, comes the responsibility of helping Humanity. God will not allow you to unleash your power until you're balanced—physically, spiritually, mentally, and emotionally and 100% in alignment with your Divine mission. Unfortunately, that process takes time."

"Okay, okay, I hear you. It doesn't mean that I like what you're saying, but I hear you," I say, slumping back in my chair.

"Well, at least you're hearing me. Now, please accept some heartfelt advice. Will you?"

"Oh, okay, what is it?"

"I know it's hard but try not to force things. Allow God's plan for you to simply unfold in His timing. Who knows? Maybe your *Toad Chronicle* series isn't your Divine mission. It may just be a stepping-stone to something far greater. Be open to all possibilities."

"Talk about putting a pin in my balloon."

"Now, come on. You know I'm not trying to shoot you down. I only want the best for you," Lily says, reaching across the table and giving my hand a reassuring squeeze. "You need to start enjoying yourself more. When was the last time you've been out on a date?"

"Um...well, I went out on a couple of dates when I was on Harbour Island last year, but that long-distance dating thing is really tough. And here, well, I can't think of anyone who I'd want to date," I reply. "And right now, I'm in the middle of a huge transformation. I don't even know what I want in a life partner anymore."

"I hear ya," she says. "So spend some quality time with your mom and those beautiful babies of yours or take a trip somewhere. Do what it is that sings from your soul, and the rest will fall into place."

Grabbing the check off the table, I say, "I'm so grateful for our friendship, Lily. I don't know what I'd do without it, or you."

"I'm happy I can be here for you. I'm so proud of the progress you've made, and the fact you've chosen to step up and into your Divine calling. Not many people choose to do so."

"Well, God hasn't exactly given me a choice," I chuckle, then hug Lily before we depart and head our separate ways.

When lunch is over, I head to my house for a short while to see my kids. That's one of the joys and benefits of having an office located less than a mile from my home. I can stop in and see my kids throughout the day.

After entering into the recreation room, I plop down on the massive leather couch. My kids immediately surround me, tails wagging, waiting for a turn to love on me. Picasso is the first to reach me followed by sweet Mattie. Tanzi, who has already crowned herself "queen of the sanctuary," growls at Mattie, who is blocking access to me.

"Hey, none of that. You need to wait your turn," I say to Tanzi while gently pushing her away to allow Mattie more room.

I sit there, lavishly petting each one of my kids as they take turns bonding with me. Yes, I now call them my *kids* because that's what they've become to me. They may have four legs, instead of two, but I love them like I would if they were my human children—one boy, Picasso, and seven girls, all sent by God to help guide and support me through my awakening.

"How have they been today?" I ask Adam after he comes back inside the recreation room.

"They've been great. The only issue I've had is with Tanzi wanting Izzie's chew toy. She was trying to pull it out of Izzie's mouth."

"Well, I'm sure Tanzi just needs time to settle in, after being bounced around. Please keep a watchful eye on her, as I don't want her injuring the other dogs."

"I will," Adam replies.

Ten minutes later, after getting showered in doggie kisses, I head back to my office. Once I'm seated at my desk, my cellphone rings. The caller ID indicates it's Holly, a friend who I hang out with on occasion.

I answer the phone and say, "Hey, Holly, how are you?"

"I'm doing well," she replies. "Listen, I know this is very last minute. But my friend, Macey, is having a small gathering of professional women tonight at a bistro in Tampa, and she needs a speaker for the event. When I told her about your book series, she was impressed and thought the ladies would enjoy hearing about it."

"Oh, gosh, that's so sweet of you. I'd be honored."

"Great! I'll pick you up at five at your office. The meeting starts at 6:30, so that should give us enough time to get there."

"See you then," I say, before hanging up the phone.

I chuckle and think, *No pressure, at all. That's less than two hours away, which is how long I have to put together an hour-long presentation for tonight's get-together.*

At 6:15, Holly and I arrive at the bistro. Once inside, I am awe-struck at the butterfly artwork hanging on every wall. "Wow! This is crazy," I say to Holly. "At lunch today, I was telling my friend, Lily, about my journey to becoming the butterfly. What are the chances?"

"You always have the most amazing stories of synchronicity, Nikki. I love hearing them," she replies, before introducing me to Macey.

Two hours later, my talk having been well-received, Holly and I are driving back home when she asks, "Do you still hear from the guy from Virginia? Mitchell, right?"

"Yep, that's him, the narcissist," I reply, waiting for the medieval door to suddenly pop open, but it doesn't. I guess the saying, "Time heals all wounds," really does hold true.

"No, I haven't heard from him for a few years now, thank goodness. I did, however, have the strangest thing happen when I rescued my first dog, Paulie. Somehow, Mitchell was tied into it, but I still don't know why." I then proceed to tell Holly about the mysterious man on the bicycle appearing on the scene, the cover of *Hope for the Flowers* on his t-shirt, and the magazine article about Mitchell's kids."

"That's unbelievable," Holly says.

"I know, I know. It's all just too weird."

And then, as if on cue, a huge sign appears in front of us.

Holly says, "Nikki, look." She points with her right hand while driving with her left. In front of us is an old, gold-colored Lincoln Continental, one which seems to stretch for miles, bearing a Virginia license plate: 54 FROG.

"Oh, my gosh!" I exclaim. "Virginia...the state where Mitchell lives. Frog...my book series. And on the very day that I give my first talk about *The Told Chronicles.* I can't make this stuff up."

But that's not all.

The next day, I contact Beth, who owns a process serving company I use for my personal injury cases. Curious about the mysterious car, I ask her to search the license plate to find out who owns it.

After giving her the plate number 54 FROG, she says, "You do know what FROG means, don't you?"

"Not exactly," I reply.

"It means, 'Fully rely upon God.' God was definitely sending you a message last night."

"Wow! I had no idea that's what it meant. Thank you so much," I say, shaken by another amazing synchronicity occurring in my life.

Then comes the clincher. About four hours later, Beth calls me back and says, "I've searched that license plate in Virginia and every other state, just to be sure. I've even searched it with the letter S. And guess what? That plate does not exist, anywhere."

"Holy cow!" I exclaim. "This is all so surreal. I really appreciate all your help."

After hanging up with Beth, I immediately call Holly and relay to her the news about the mysterious car. "That's totally crazy," she says. "I know you've told me stories about the signs God sends you, but you definitely made me a believer last night."

"Well, thanks for bearing witness to it. Without you there, I might have thought the car wasn't real," I say.

"Have you figured out what the number fifty-four means?"

"No, not yet, but I will let you know if, and when, I do. Have a great night."

"You too, Nikki," she says, before ending the call.

After hanging up with Holly, it hits me—the conversation I had with Lily not too long ago where she said that God would guide me using signs, synchronicities, and number sequences. I also recall a friend telling me one time that every letter in the alphabet corresponds to a different number, starting with A=1, B=2, and so forth.

Ushing this methodology, I decide to calculate the letters in my first name (something I've never done until now): N=14, I=9, K=11, K=11, and I=9. Lo and behold, when I add them all together, they equal "54."

"I can't believe this," I say to myself, awe-struck by my discovery. "God was speaking directly to me the other night, literally addressing me by my name and letting me know to fully rely upon Him."

Sitting back in my chair, I reflect upon yesterday's serendipitous chain of events which is too overwhelming to deny—one sign, after another—boom, boom, boom. Obviously, God is trying to get my attention, once again. I guess it's time I stop questioning Him and embrace the path He's setting out for me with unwavering faith.

Chapter Forty-Eight

Tanzi has been home for three weeks now and as hoped, she is settling into her new life (no more roof top incidents!) as are all of her Turkish sisters, who love being U.S. dog citizens. What a far cry their lives are today from a little over a year ago, when they aimlessly wandered the streets of Turkey.

Thankfully, everyone is getting along splendidly, although I'm sure there will be times in the not-so-distant future when a fight or two will ensue. That's just dogs! Not unlike humans, they have times when they just don't get along. I pray, though, that a fight won't ever result in a permanent split like what's happened between my sister and me.

As for my dear, sweet Lucky, I've since contacted three Turkish lawyers, all of whom have refused to take my case against Nadia. Not a single one has felt a *dog* is worthy of pursuing legal action. "Vermin" is what one lawyer called Lucky. I wanted to email him back a big, fat "fuck you" but stopped myself.

So for now, I've put the idea of getting Lucky home on the back burner. Eight or nine months from now, I will travel to Turkey and break her out of Nadia's kennels myself, if I have to. Only problem is that I don't exactly know where Nadia's kennels are located, as she keeps the location a secret (for some strange reason). Someone, somewhere, though, will be able to assist me when the time comes. I feel it in my every bone.

It's now December, and with the Christmas holiday season rapidly approaching, I decide to take Lily up on her suggestion that I take trip. The personal injury market typically slows down the week before Christmas and for two weeks after, so this will be the perfect time for me to get away. Plus, it will do me some good to be gone from Tarpon Springs during this time of the year which is typically a tough time for me emotionally.

For the past couple of years, the German Christmas markets have been on my very long bucket list. The Bavarian region of Germany is where the fairy tale about the princess and the frog began (it was written by the Brothers Grimm in1812), so I feel a huge calling to travel there, hoping it will unblock my writer's block and allow me to move forward with the revise of my *The Toad Chronicles* book.

As a home base, I choose Munich for six nights, since it has an international airport and is close distance by train to the cities I wish to visit. I reserve a room at an adorable, boutique hotel that has been recently refurbished and is located within walking distance to the train station.

Wanting her company, I ask my mother to join me, but she's afraid she won't be able to take the cold. Truthfully, I'm not sure I will either because I'm a sunshine-kind-of girl, having lived the majority of my life in Florida.

This being a last-minute idea, I find myself scurrying to get everything in order at work and home before I depart on December 15th. One evening after work, I run out and purchase some winter clothing for my trip, including an insulated jacket, a couple of sweaters, some thermal underwear and socks, along with a thick, wool scarf. Using my Delta frequent flyer miles, I also book a round-trip ticket, paying only a small fee for the flight. Miraculously, the trip comes together, thanks to the help of Clare and Adam.

The morning of my flight, Adam and I review a lengthy list of all the dogs' wants and needs. I hand him some emergency money, then pet each dog several times and tearfully kiss them goodbye, promising to return home in a week's time.

"Go, go," Adam says to me. "You're going to be late for your flight. I promise to take care of your kids."

"Thanks for being so good to them, and to me. I'll call you tomorrow from Munich," I say, before grabbing my bags and throwing them into the back of the Rover. I feel like I'm abandoning my kids but know they will be well-cared for in my absence.

Sixteen hours later, I land at the Munich International Airport, blurry-eyed and numb from a lack of sleep. I grab my duffel bag from the baggage carousel, change some money, and hail a taxi.

Shortly before 9:00 a.m., I arrive at the hotel, hoping to check-in early, but my room is still occupied. For the next two hours, I nap restlessly in a chair of the hotel lobby until the front desk notifies me that I can finally check-in. After the bellman delivers my duffel bag to my room, I take a quick shower, change into some warm clothing, and call Adam to let him know that I've arrived safely.

Map in hand, and after a quick bite to eat in the hotel café, I wander out into the streets of Munich. My plan is to explore the markets of Munich today and travel via train the following days to Salzburg, Augsburg, Regensburg, and Nuremberg with the highlight being a trip to the Neuschwanstein Castle built by Ludwig II of Bavaria.

As I stroll through the markets over the coming days, I am awe-struck by all the beauty surrounding me. It's like walking through a winter wonderland, a sort of dream world, as there are white lights and decorations hanging everywhere.

In each city I visit, Christmas stalls are set up usually in or around the central market area. They are filled with all sorts of amazing items, including handicrafts, ornaments, table linens, home-made sausages, cheeses, fresh breads, pastries, candies, and what quickly becomes a favorite of mine—glühwein, a drink of hot spiced wine. Just what I need on a cold winter's day!

Throughout the week, I attend a number of performances, all spectacular, my favorite being the carolers I listen to late one afternoon in

Salzburg, one of my favorite European cities. Back in college, when my mom and I backpacked through Europe, we had stopped in Salzburg for two nights. It was an enjoyable stay, as it was early June back then, and the tulips had been in full bloom all over the city. I promised myself that I would one day return to this beautiful city.

During my travels, I also meet a lot of interesting people, from all walks of life, either while I'm on the trains, eating at one of the restaurants, or when walking around the markets. One night, while I'm at a beer hall, a group of strangers invites me to join them at their table. We have an absolute blast, drinking, singing, and just plain having fun—total strangers, brought together by the spirit of Christmas and the hands of fate.

At every almost turn, synchronistic signs for my *Toad Chronicles* series appear in my path. It's like I'm following a roadmap God has laid out for me, and it's a beautiful, awe-inspiring one. All these signs, coupled with the wonderful people I meet and the sites that I see, cause me to feel a deep, spiritual connection with the region—like I've lived here before in another lifetime.

While en route to the Neuschwanstein Castle located in southern Bavaria near Füssen, I am totally blown away. A man stops me on the street, hands me a small Prince-Charming frog figurine, and says in very broken English, "Here, for you." I stand there astonished by this incredible moment of serendipity. *How can this be?* I think, before turning to thank the man, who has already disappeared from my sight.

After putting the figurine into my bag, I start the long hike up the steep hill toward the castle thinking, *God is so amazing. When you open up to His greatness and really connect with Him, He sends the most amazing signs. It's like following a lighted path toward a most glorious destination.*

By the end of the week, the empty tote bag that I've brought from home is filled with gifts for my mom and my employees as well as many souvenirs for myself. In Regensburg, I purchase several hand-blown ornaments depicting Prince Charming as a frog, while in Munich I buy a unique, antique music box with tiny frogs on the lid. They all symbolize my magical trip to the winter wonderland where the fairy tale about the princess and the frog began.

Chapter Forty-Nine

Shortly after returning home from Munich, a mutual friend introduces me to a woman living in the Bahamas, who rescues animals off the street. Inspired by the work she does, I donate toward the vetting expenses for a sweet Bahamian potcake, who has sustained a fracture to one of her legs after being abused by her former owner. I also help to coordinate the transport of one of the woman's rescue dogs boarding in my area to his forever home in southern Georgia.

The rescue woman has also posted photos of four other dogs, two older and two younger ones, who are living on the street in Nassau. These poor souls desperately need to be rescued and placed into foster care, before something tragic happens to them. Every single day, they are fighting to survive, being faced with the harsh elements, a lack of food, and fights with other dogs. They have also found an enemy in a local shopkeeper, who has threatened to kill them if they aren't promptly removed from the area.

Of course, the photos tug at my heartstrings as does every photo of a dog who has been neglected or abused. I swear, I used to be so tough-hearted. Now, I cry at the drop of a hat—part of my awakening, I do believe.

What really catches my eye, though, is that the rescue woman wants to send the dogs to a foster place called "Fairy Tails Fostering" located in Princeton, West Virginia. Having just returned from the original land of fairy tales, and the fact my character in *The Toad Chronicles* series is searching for Prince Charming, I take this as a sure sign that I am destined to help them.

I immediately contact the rescue woman and offer to assist in transporting the dogs. After numerous messages back and forth, we devise a plan. She and the dogs will fly via Bahamasair from Nassau into Orlando International Airport, where I will meet her, pick the dogs up, and have them driven to West Virginia by a transporter.

Two weeks later, Dreamer and Pebble arrive in Orlando without a glitch. My mom and I make the two-hour drive to the airport and pick them up but when I meet the dogs, I'm heart-stricken. These are old souls, dogs between ten to thirteen years old, an eternity for a dog to live on the streets without the warmth and love of human touch.

When the second shipment of dogs arrives, I notice that Kaleo, a younger, gray-colored, brindle mix, has a lot of gunk in his eyes, indicating he may have a serious underlying infection. Concerned about his well-being, I contact the rescue woman in Nassau and let her know that I'm delaying the dogs' transport to West Virginia.

The next day, I take Kaleo to my vet, who examines him and says he is too sick to travel. Not only does Kaleo have heartworms and a severe upper respiratory infection, but he also has sarcoptic mange which is contagious to other dogs. My vet recommends quarantine for five weeks. To avoid the cost of two separate transports to West Virginia, I cancel the transport for Dreamer, Pebble, and Leo, who will now stay with me while Kaleo receives treatment and recovers.

A few days later, I decide to take Dreamer to my office to help relieve Adam of the stress of having three new dogs to care for. While I'm out running a quick errand, I leave Dreamer at the office with Clare and my other assistants.

Well, within minutes of being gone, Clare calls and says, "Hey, Nikki, your new dog, Dreamer, has been howling at the top of his lungs ever since you left. The manager of the bank next door came over to check on us, worried something might be wrong. That's how loud he is."

"Dreamer's not my *new* dog, Clare. I have no intention of keeping him There's a foster already lined up for him in West Virginia. Tell him to cool his jets. I'll be back to the office shortly."

"Uh, I hate to tell you, but this dog is totally smitten with you," she says. "This love affair between the two of you is written in the stars. You'll see."

I'm not as convinced as Clare, though. My Turkish princesses arrived just a few months ago, so I'm not ready to add another dog to my pack, at least not yet. But as the weeks forge on, and Dreamer settles into his surroundings, it becomes obvious that he wants my home to be his home, my heart to be his heart. Not only does he howl when we are apart, he scales the cement staircase late one afternoon—the same one Tanzi climbed a few months earlier—and ends up on the tile roof above the portico. He then jumps off the roof (about a ten foot drop), wanders to the back gate where I'm unloading groceries from the Rover, and stands there, looking at me with this humongous grin on his face.

I could get mad at him, I suppose, but I think about what the rescue woman in Nassau previously said about him. She described him as the most depressed street dog she'd ever seen. According to her, he wouldn't even lift his head when eating out of the food bowl she would leave for him. He had a look of despair in his eyes, as if life had already crushed him.

Most likely, he was a "throw away" dog, meaning he was once *loosely* owned (a common life pattern for Bahamian potcakes) before being discarded out onto the street. So to see him come to life is incredibly heartwarming. Still, despite his obvious affection for me, and the fact he is blossoming under my care, I'm not sure if I'm ready for another dog.

Then one evening, I'm sitting on my family room couch, working on my book. Pebble and Leo are fast asleep in the master suite, while the other dogs are bedded down in the guest house and recreation room. Dreamer, on the other hand, is lying next to the double doors of the family room, leading out into the courtyard.

Wanting some background noise, I turn on the TV and DVD player and begin watching *Under the Tuscan Sun*, one of my all-time favorite movies. It's rare that I watch television, so the DVD for the movie is still sitting in the player, left there from the last time I watched it. Its theme resonates strongly with me, so I find myself watching it, time and again, looking to glean clues to help guide me through life.

In the movie, Diane Lane stars as Francesca, a divorced writer, who impulsively buys a run-down villa in Tuscany, hoping it will lead to a change in her life. While renovating the villa, she is taken on a journey of self-discovery, where she learns a great deal about herself.

One evening, a snake crawls into her bedroom, and she calls upon Signore Martini, the realtor who sold her the villa, to come and remove it. As they're talking, Francesca tearfully admits that she feels stupid for buying a house for a life that she doesn't even have. Signore Martini then asks her why she bought the house, and she replies she still wants things in her life, like a family and a wedding.

Seeking to comfort her, Signore Martini tells the story of train tracks that were built over an impossibly steep, very high part of the Alps known as the Semmering. The tracks, as he tells the story, were built even before there was a train in existence that could make the trip. They were built, knowing one day the train would come.

When the renovations to the villa are finished, Francesca hosts a wedding for one of the construction workers. During the celebration, a man named "Ed" stops at the villa and asks to meet the American writer who lives there (meaning "Francesca"). From there, the movie switches to inside the villa where Ed, Francesca, and her friends (now considered her family) are gathered around the dining table celebrating the holidays, implying Francesca's train has finally come.

At the end of the movie, in reflecting upon her life, Francesca says: "What are four walls, anyway? They are what they contain. The house protects the dreamer. Unthinkably good things can happen, even late in the game. It's such a surprise."

As the credits begin to roll, despite watching the movie at least two dozen times before, tears stream down my face. I think of my own struggles and the renovations still ongoing at my home. Purchased in 2003, the same year the movie was released, my home was considered the town's biggest eye sore (and renovation challenge). The house was shown close to three hundred times before I finally took the plunge and bought it. Now, eight years later, the renovations are far from over, and my personal transformation is still incomplete.

Stupid, that's how I feel some days. Just like Francesca, I bought a house for a life that I didn't even have. I'm forty-four years old and still waiting for my train to come. Either it's made a wrong turn, or it's crashed and burned along the way.

I sigh heavily and think, *Or maybe my train has come. Maybe the dogs God has sent my way are what the four walls of my house are meant to contain. Maybe a husband and children aren't in God's Divine plan for me.*

Wiping away my tears, I look down at Dreamer, who is sleeping soundly on the dog bed I bought for him that is covered with a soft, Sherpa blanket. There is something so incredibly spiritual about him, something so serene. What an amazing soul of a dog to have risen up from the ashes at an older age.

Right now, he has the biggest smile on his face (if dogs can smile, that is). He's looks so incredibly happy, like he knows his train has finally come. Deep down, I know this, too. Dreamer is where he belongs—in my home, safe from the perils of the outside world. My house is protecting the dreamer.

Watching *Under the Tuscan Sun* with Dreamer lying next to me, I realize something else, something really profound. God sent Dreamer to me as a messenger (a Goddog, mind you)—to remind me that good things can happen in life, even late in the game. A really big surprise can occur, when it's least expected.

I power off my laptop, give Dreamer a good rubdown, and head off to bed, thanking God for the beautiful journey of awakening He is taking me on. Every step of the way, He is teaching me that behind every heartache, hardship, difficulty, and challenge, there lies a blessing waiting to be found. And my Goddogs are just some of the many blessings He has bestowed my way.

About Book Two

Set to release Winter 2023, join Karis in book two of her Goddogs series which is a continuation of her journey of awakening. Dreamer's story also unfolds along with the stories of Picasso, Izzie, Zoie, and Karis' Turkish princesses. Of course, several new Goddogs cross Karis' path in a most miraculous way and join her on her journey.

Also, read about the amazing recovery of Lucky, who, after many years, finally makes her way out of Turkey and on to the Karis Animal Sanctuary located in Tarpon Springs, Florida.

Lucky, U.S. Dog Citizen

Visit Tail-Life.com

If you would like to connect with other animal lovers from around the world, then visit https://Tail-Life.com which is Karis' merchandise and media site, devoted to people, pets, not politics.

Acknowledgements

To my mother and father, who live on in spirit, thank you for always being a guiding light of inspiration. Together, you were my compass during life's many storms. You were my inspiration and biggest cheerleaders who loved me unconditionally. Without your love and support through the years, I never would have achieved my dream of becoming a published author, inspirational speaker, and creative entrepreneur.

To my rescue cats and dogs, who hail from around the world, I am blessed beyond measure to have you making this journey of life with me. Your unconditional love is a constant reminder to always love and accept myself, faults, foibles, imperfections, and all. And to all of my animals who have already passed on, thank you for continuing to guide me from above. I feel your spirit with me, each and every day.

To my friends, both near and far, I deeply appreciate all the support you gave to me during my long and arduous journey of awakening while becoming the person I was always meant to be. Your belief in me gave me hope during some of my darkest hours; and for that, I remain eternally grateful.

To all those persons, who lent their time, talents, and energy to my creative projects, I thank you from the bottom of my heart. Without you, my dreams would have never become a reality.

To all those persons, who I once perceived to be my enemies, haters, and detractors, I honor you for being some of my greatest teachers. The pressures you placed upon me in various ways helped to polish me and make me shine like a diamond. I love you, forgive you, and wish you only the best in life. I truly believe that every relationship, good or bad, comes into our life to teach us a valuable lesson, and I am most grateful for the lessons you taught me.

And to my sweet dog, Lulu, who traveled with me many times to the island of Eleuthera where I sought inspiration and quiet time to write, thank you for being my kindred spirit and by my side, as I penned the words of my series. I love you, baby girl!

Inspiring Messages

In March of 2009, at the onset of her awakening, Karis began writing inspiring messages and posting them on her social media accounts. Ten years later, in 2019, she published a collection of her messages titled, *Becoming Grace – 800 Inspiring Messages*. She also published a collection of her animal messages titled, *Heartwarming Animal Messages*.

Via her inspiring messages, Karis shares the life lessons she has learned and the wisdom she has gained, helping to empower others to rise above any challenges or difficulties they may be facing. To purchase either collection, visit Tail-Life.com. Get 20% of an e-book of either collection at Tail-Life.com, using coupon code: MESSAGES20OFF.

Here is a sample of Karis' messages:

Happiness is available to everyone,
not just the rich, the educated, or a privileged few.
Reach for it, embrace it, and make it your very own.

Nothing ever gets accomplished by sitting around
and waiting for others to accomplish things for you.
Get into the action and accomplish things for yourself.

Rid your life of drama. Squash it!
Stamp it out! Get rid of it for good!
Once you do, your life will head in a positive direction.

Humanity isn't defined by
the amount of money someone has in the bank,
the number of diplomas hanging on the walls,
or the list of achievements on a resume.
It's defined by the amount of compassion filling the heart.

In a stormy sea filled with hatred, fear, and confusion,
be a calming voice of love, tolerance, and reason.

Gender, race, religion, and economic status
don't deeply divide our world.
It's the invisible walls and artificial boundaries we build
that prevent unity and peace.

Taking a risk and a leap of faith can be scary.
When you finally find the courage to leap,
your belief in yourself and your ability to succeed
will be the wings that allow you to fly.

Each day you awaken, each breath that is taken,
is a glorious gift from above.
Celebrate each and every day as being a beautiful blessing.

Love is a place in your heart where...
Happiness reigns, peace flourishes,
compassion flows, and hope springs eternal.
Most of all, it's a place where judgment never rules.

Allow the storyline of your life to unfold
with perfect rhythm and timing.

When faced with what seems like an insurmountable challenge,
remember that like all challenges before it,
you will rise to the occasion and accomplish great things.

You're capable of accomplishing the most amazing things.
All you have to do is believe in yourself.
While the road to success may be bumpy at times,
the sense of triumph you'll feel once
you've crossed the finish line will make it all worth the effort.

Reclaim your self-esteem!
Wherever it may have gone or whoever may have taken it,
the simple fact remains—it belongs back with you.

Our world has become a highly toxic place...
from our waterways to our food sources
to our emotions and to our spirits.
Please do your part to clean up your little corner of the world.

Wake with conviction to change your life for the better.
No one is responsible for bringing about
those changes except yourself.

Behind every heartache, hardship, difficulty, or challenge,
there lies a blessing waiting to be found.
Seek to discover your blessings!

Take responsibility for what you speak.
Just as sticks and stones can break a person's bones,
words can break another person's spirit.

The world will never change as long as
ordinary people believe they are just that—ordinary.
Change comes when ordinary people understand
just how truly extraordinary they are.

Do some emotional housekeeping!
Once you do, you'll free your heart, mind, body, and soul
of the past to allow the wonderful opportunities
of the future to shine through.

For today, count the many wonderful blessings
and opportunities present in your life.
As for yesterday, give thanks you successfully made
it through to see the light of today.
As for tomorrow, well, don't worry about
what tomorrow might bring.
If you're looking ahead to tomorrow,
you're missing out on all the many wonderful blessings
and opportunities present in your life today.

The greatest partnership the human race
can make is with the animals.
It's from this partnership that love and compassion for all
of God's creations will flourish and grow.

If you had a choice between having your pets
or all the riches in the world,
you should choose your pets each and every time.
While riches may come and go in your life,
the love of your pet will always remain constant and real.

About the Author

Nikki Karis, whose given name is Nikki Marie Kavouklis, grew up in Tarpon Springs, Florida. As a child, many people, including her parents and teachers, recognized that Karis possessed a special gift for connecting with people via the written and spoken word.

Karis obtained her BA degree and later, her juris doctorate degree, both from the University of Florida. After graduating from law school, Karis returned to her hometown to practice law. Karis started her own law firm in 1999 which grew into a successful practice. In January of 2019, she closed her active practice to pursue her dream of becoming a published author and launching an inspirational company with associated merchandise to help empower others.

Karis enjoys spending time with her rescue cats and dogs, helping humans and animals, researching, reading, traveling, collecting art, and decorating her circa 1925 home. Her future plans include building a home and an animal rescue center on Eleuthera, where she frequently retreats to write, and growing Finding Zeni, Inc. and its associated projects into a successful, caring, and compassionate company with a mission to uplift and inspire others.

For more information about Karis and her inspiring projects, visit: www.NikkiKaris.com (Karis' official site); www.Tail-Life.com (media and merchandise site for humans & pets); www.PetSoulsTV.com (Goddogs book site); www.LetsEscapetheSwamp.com (Karis' other book series); and www.T1Rise.com (Karis' activism site).

Books by Nikki Karis

Escape the Swamp (formerly, The Toad Chronicles) –

Escape the Swamp (published under pen name of "Giana Solomon")

Goddogs –

Goddogs

God + Dogs to the Rescue (junior edition of Goddogs)

Heartwarming Animal Messages

Becoming Grace –

Becoming Grace – 800 Inspiring Messages

Illuminate Your Life

Uplift Your Spirit

Energize Your Soul

Relax Your Body

Stimulate Your Mind

500 Powerful Affirmations – Think, Act, and Feel Positive

Purchase Escape the Swamp

If you enjoyed Goddogs and want to read more of Karis' inspiring tales, purchase book one of her Escape the Swamp series. For more info about the series, visit: www.LetsEscapetheSwamp.com.

Made in United States
North Haven, CT
17 April 2023

35565612R00147